ECOSHOT

ECOSHOT

HOW AMERICA CAN WIN
THE CLEAN INDUSTRIAL
REVOLUTION AGAINST CHINA

STUART POWELL

NEW DEGREE PRESS

ECOSHOT

How America Can Win the Clean Industrial Revolution Against China

ISBN   978-1-64137-196-4   *Paperback*

978-1-64137-197-1   *Ebook*

*To my wife **Andrea**, who was patient with me while I spent long nights and weekends in the library working on this book.*

*To **Mom**, who taught me to leave a room better than I found it. I've now expanded that meaning to leave the Earth better than I found it.*

*To **Dad**, who taught me stewardship through his mission work across Central America to help those who needed it the most. I've now found my own stewardship and mission work to address the biggest issue of my generation – climate change.*

To people who helped me throughout this process:
Hunter Ricks, Keith Siracuse, Alex Bozmoski, Katherine Hamilton, Jigar Shah, James McDermott, Jim Tolbert, and many others.

CONTENTS

INTRODUCTION

———

"Every problem is an opportunity in disguise."

—JOHN ADAMS, FOUNDING FATHER AND THE
SECOND PRESIDENT OF THE UNITED STATES

On October 4, 1957, the Soviet Union launched Sputnik, the first satellite, into space in the height of the Cold War. The launch was a visual warning that America had lost its technological edge. The Sputnik crisis triggered to the Space Race between the Soviet Union and the United States. Instead of retreating into fear, America put forward a bold mission toward the stars. On September 12, 1962, President John F. Kennedy made a bold promise that America would put about putting a man on the moon by the end of the decade, despite not having any of the technologies in place to accomplish that goal. Less than eight years later on July 20, 1969, America accomplished that vision by landing Neil Armstrong and Buzz Aldrin on the moon. We succeeded because we had a national vision with a clear mission.

We have now entered a new Space Race, with a new industry and a new competitor. China has become a world leader in trade, evident by America's trade war with China beginning in 2018. President Trump is going head-to-head with Chinese President Xi Jinping over trade relationships by implementing significant tariffs on Chinese imported goods. One of the first industries impacted by the trade war is the clean energy industry, with a tariff placed on imported solar panels.

China now has an insatiable energy demand and an exploding emissions problem. The country's leadership has responded with massive investments in clean technology and is becoming a world leader in clean energy and electric vehicles. Although the US has spent decades performing basic research and development behind solar panels, but China has provided massive support to their domestic businesses, and now over 60 percent of the world's solar panels are manufactured in China. Furthermore, half of global electric cars sales were in China in 2016.[1] Even though China is the biggest emitter of carbon emissions, it is also the world's biggest investor in clean technologies.

The Sputnik event sparked a change in the mind and hearts of the American public and politicians to a new vision. America now needs that same wake-up call for action, so we can become a global competitor in the world's next industrial revolution — the *Clean Revolution*.

Whether or not the United States remains in the international climate agreement, the world is moving toward a goal of reducing emissions. The commitment to withdraw from the Paris Climate Agreement tells the world, especially China, that America does not want to lead the world in next-generation clean technology in energy and mobility. President Xi stated that China would take the "driving seat in international cooperation to respond to climate change."[2] China is racing to innovate and sell clean technologies to the world in the new space race.

What America needs now is a moonshot goal for cleantech, and we need to get this EcoShot launched today before we fall behind the technology curve. Rather than China selling us solar panels, America should be selling clean energy and electric vehicles to China to address their pollution problems. In the first half of the book ,I discuss how China made significant advancements in cleantech through supportive industrial policies. In the second half, I discuss how national leaders can support American scientists, investors, businesses, and jobs by putting in effective policies through innovation, tax reform, regulatory reform, and state grants. It's time to turn the tides and create a vision for the largest job and wealth opportunity in our lifetime. "Eco" means environmental, but Eco now also means the world's greatest <u>eco</u>nomic opportunity.

The global movement toward a clean economy won't cause an economic disruption. The Clean Revolution means the development of American innovation, energy independence, clean jobs, and economic prosperity. As noted in the opening quote, America needs to see China's pollution problem and the world's emissions problem as a massive and global economic opportunity. Let's stop looking backward and start looking forward. Let's mobilize as a nation and implement an EcoShot.

PART 1

AN INTERNATIONAL SHIFT

CHAPTER 1

THE NEXT INDUSTRIAL REVOLUTION

———

"The Stone Age did not end because the world ran out of stones, and the Oil Age will not end because we run out of oil."

—AHMED ZAKI YAMANI, FORMER MINISTER

OF OIL FOR SAUDI ARABIA

History repeats itself. The battle between human tribes was constantly over a competition for resources with the victor usually being the tribe with the greater technology. The Stone, Bronze, and Iron Age were defined by who had the weapons of the strongest material. Later, the First and Second Industrial Revolutions were defined by the nations that had best innovations to outcompete the others. Competition in the animal kingdom is governed by "survival of the fittest," and for tribes and then nations, having the most modern technology led to the *thriving of the fittest*. Each industrial revolution leaves a clear winner at the end, and the Third Industrial Revolution, which could be called the "Clean Revolution" to achieve a cleaner global economy, will be no different. The question remains who will lead the Clean Revolution into the largest economic opportunity of the twenty-first century—the United States or China.

THE NEXT INDUSTRIAL REVOLUTION

The Clean Revolution is the natural next transition in the evolution of civilization. Human history has progressed through the Stone Age, the Bronze Age, the Iron Age, and currently the Fossil Fuel Age. Access to affordable and accessible fossil fuels is a strategic advantage for countries that had abundant industry to power their economies. We are now entering the Silicon Age – defined by advanced technologies run by silicon, including communications (computer chips), mobility (computers in cars), and clean energy (solar panels). The Silicon Age is sparking this Third Industrial Revolution – new innovations leading to new ways to power our economy. We are now at the dawn of this era of human history.

Moving our industries away from fossil fuels will differentiate old economies from new economies. The countries that embrace these technologies will advance their own economies, and the ones that don't will get left behind. It's truly a serendipitous time in history. On one hand, we have an existential climate issue that will impact us, our children, and humanity for future generations; on the other, we also have a new revolution coming with the advent of affordable clean technologies: wind, solar, batteries, and more.

People who don't believe we'll move to clean energy and electric mobility are of same mindset at those who said several decades ago that computers in every home were a pipe dream—when we now know the advancement of the internet has led to trillions of dollars of new wealth. Moving to clean energy and electric vehicles, while moving away from high resource dependence on other nations, will create a competitive advantage for nations that embrace these technologies. Human history amply demonstrates that embracing new tools, technologies, and innovations leads to significant advancements of nations. The industrial revolutions have brought down the cost of goods, while spreading the goods far and wide.

With the discovery of fossil fuels, civilization entered into the Fossil Fuel Age, which included both the First and Second Industrial Revolutions. With the discovery and mass use of coal, society entered the **First Industrial Revolution**, which occurred in Britain in the mid-1700s through the mid-1800s.

The energy revolution was triggered by the invention of the steam-powered engine by James Watt, which allowed new production methods for industries such as textiles, agriculture, and more. Human-intensive products were cheaper to produce with machinery powered by fossil fuels, and with this same technology, transportation was revolutionized as steam engines were able to transport goods vast distances by rail. The energy revolution went hand in hand with the transportation revolution, and the combination of these twin revolutions made Britain the world Superpower due to the massive economic growth.

During the **Second Industrial Revolution**, the United States led the way with the energy revolution powered by cheap coal and oil available in the US. Centralized electricity flourished with the inventions by Thomas Edison and Nikola Tesla, eventually leading to a national grid. The discovery of cheap oil also led the transportation revolution, with the advent of Henry Ford's mass-produced Model T. Texas led the energy revolution with oil, which fueled the transportation revolution in Detroit.

As with the First and Second Industrial Revolutions, the Clean Revolution is now being powered by revolutionary innovations in energy and transportation. The First and Second Industrial Revolutions were both part of the Fossil Fuel Age, but the Third Industrial Revolution is born of the Silicon Age. Silicon powers the computer chips in our cell phones, laptops, tablets, and now cars. The successful scaling of silicon production from our communications industry has caused solar panel costs to plummet, becoming competitive with coal and natural gas. Large-scale (utility-scale) scale solar projects are already cheaper than new coal and gas plants over the lifetime of the plant in most regions of the US due to the 88 percent drop in price since 2009.[1] In fact, California passed legislation in 2018 to power its economy with 50 percent renewable energy (solar and wind) by 2026 and 100 percent clean carbon-free energy by 2045 – clean energy was not defined by law, but it could possibly include options such as solar, wind, nuclear, hydropower and fossil fuel plants with carbon capture technologies. This is a big deal, considering California is the world's fifth largest economy on its own.[2] The energy revolution is here.

Innovation is happening in mobility as well, thanks to the significant development coming from the communications industries. The smartphone industry, birthed here in the US first with Blackberry and then transformed with Apple, is now transforming the automotive industry. The lithium-ion technology found in our phones and computers is now driving innovation (no pun intended) the electrification of transportation, as we've seen with Tesla. In 2018, Tesla's Model 3 was estimated to cost around $190 per kWh, which is about a 70% drop in the last six years.[3] Batteries are expected to reach parity with combustion engines by 2024, according to Bloomberg New Energy Finance.[4]

Exponential advancements in various technologies are moving society toward the Clean Revolution. With computer chips, we see Moore's Law—the doubling of computer power every eighteen months—has drastically reduced the costs of more advanced technology. In the past decade, we have seen similar trends in solar cells, wind turbines, and battery technology. Swanson's Law holds for solar: the cost of solar drops 20 percent for every doubling of production, so the more solar we put on our roofs and land, the quicker the costs will come down to benefit our society. Having the right policies, support, and messaging by our government leaders locally and nationally will encourage private sector investments to accelerate this cost curve down.

We have the opportunity to make the Clean Revolution happen here in America. As it was in the First Industrial Revolution, Texas is once again one of the leaders in the modern-day energy revolution, as Texas is now the #1 state in wind energy. California leads in installed solar due to strong public support and now the increasingly favorable economics. In transportation, Detroit is beginning to catch up with electric vehicles, but once again, California leads America as the home of Tesla, which became one of the top five best-selling sedans in the second half of 2018.[5] Ford and

GM have announced investments in the electric future of the mobility revolution, but Detroit will have to catch up to the tech capital of the world.

THE LEADER OF THE CLEAN REVOLUTION

The layout of this book focuses on the three C's: Carbon Emissions, China, and Cleantech. The world has come together to sign the Paris Climate Agreement to address climate change by reducing global **carbon emissions**. Countries around the world are looking to reduce their emissions, including transitioning their biggest carbon-intensive sectors, particularly for electricity and transportation. **China** is also looking for cleaner sources of energy, as the country has growing pollution issues coming from their sea of coal plants and gas-powered cars.

China is a massive market, with a massively growing economy and middle class. Even though China is the largest carbon emitter, the Asian powerhouse is making significant progress in cleantech—like solar, wind, and electric vehicles—through government support and mandates.

In the second half of the book, we will discuss how the US can create a vision and put the right policies in place for our domestic **cleantech** industry for this massive economic opportunity. Both the $2 trillion global energy sector[6] and $2 trillion automotive industry[7] will both grow rapidly over the coming decades as the world population and the middle class grows significantly, especially in Asia and Africa. America would be making a major mistake by missing out on this $4 trillion economic transition.

I spoke with Jim McDermott, who is the Managing Director of US Renewables Group and founder/former CEO of the publicly-traded company Stamps.com. He was the first person I spoke with for the book, and he really put it in a great perspective: *"Absolute fortunes are going to be made here. I think people still think it's the domain of the Birkenstock crowd. I got into this because I believe we still have to do something. And we're talking about the global energy industry – there's so much money to be made. The people who get this are the people in Texas – the red state Republicans get it, and they're piling in."*

As Jim alluded to, the Clean Revolution is also a Green Revolution – there is a lot of "green" (money) in clean energy now, but that will just continue to grow exponentially as the world moves to a new clean economy. Cleantech isn't a "red" or "blue" issue – soon enough it will be a "red, white, and blue" issue as Americans, governments, and businesses see the positive impacts on their wallets. The question remains who will lead this Third Industrial Revolution. America was responsible for a significant amount of research and development that went into solar panels, but now China is the leading panel manufacturer across the globe. In the following chapters, we will dive into how China put the right policies, support, and incentives in place to spark a clean energy revolution, leading to over three million clean energy jobs.[8]

Furthermore, the US started the electric car evolution with the research into battery technologies, but now China is the leader in electric vehicle production and sales due to their growing pollution challenges and industrial policies. China is the world's biggest automotive market and is already the world's biggest electric car market. In the first half of the book, we will take a deep dive into how China has made significant progress in the last decade with trade, clean energy, and electric transportation. Can America catch up, or if China will be the leader of the Clean Revolution?

	ENERGY	TRANSPORTATION	LEADER
1st Industrial Revolution	Coal	Steam-powered rail	United Kingdom
2nd Industrial Revolution	Coal & oil	Gas car	United States
3rd Industrial Revolution	Clean energy	Clean mobility	China or US?

The world is moving forward, and I believe it's time for the US to take a leadership position in the new economic transition. In my research for this book, I have come to believe

China is currently ahead of the US, as I will lay out in the following chapters. Climate change isn't the reason we should ignore this problem, it's the reason we should embrace and support American innovation to be a world leader to solve this global problem. The world is moving forward, and we need to be at the head of the table. The Paris Climate Agreement is a clear market signal that the world is moving away from fossil fuels and toward a clean future. In the next chapter, we'll dive into the monumental international agreement, which is going to accelerate this Clean Revolution over the next decade and beyond.

KEY TAKEAWAYS

- **Silicon Age**: Humans have seen a transition over time with a key theme of embracing new resources and advancements, as we saw with the Stone, Bronze, and Iron Ages. We are now transitioning from the Fossil Fuel Age to the Silicon Age, where our energy and transportation sectors are evolving, with wind, solar, electric cars, and more.

- **Clean Revolution**: The First Industrial Revolution occurred in the UK, where the abundance of coal led to the steam-powered engine that significantly advanced the country's industrial sector. The steam engine was also put on rails to allow railroads to move goods across vast regions. Eventually, the Second Industrial Revolution evolved in the US, where cheap oil in Texas led to a new energy source for the American economic growth. Abundant oil eventually led to the automotive industry in Detroit. History repeats itself — these industrial revolutions led to massive economic growth through transforming the energy and transportation sectors. The same will happen for the Third Industrial Revolution — called the Clean Revolution. The energy and automotive combine into a massive $4 trillion opportunity now, which will continue to grow in the future.

- **The C's**: The themes of this book will evolve around the need to address the Climate by innovating Cleantech and determining whether the US will win the cleantech race against China. The world has a signed a global agreement to address carbon emissions, so either the US or China will lead this global economic transition.

"Coal, oil and gas are called fossil fuels because they are mostly made of the fossil remains of beings from long ago. The chemical energy within them is a kind of stored sunlight originally accumulated by ancient plants. Our civilization runs by burning the remains of humble creatures who inhabited the Earth hundreds of millions of years before the first humans came on the scene. Like some ghastly cannibal cult, we subsist on the dead bodies of our ancestors and distant relatives."

—CARL SAGAN—AMERICAN ASTRONOMER,

COSMOLOGIST, AND ASTROPHYSICIST

CHAPTER 2

A GLOBAL SHIFT

—

"So, let us not be blind to our differences--but let us also direct attention to our common interests and to the means by which those differences can be resolved. And if we cannot end now our differences, at least we can help make the world safe for diversity. For, in the final analysis, our most basic common link is that we all inhabit this small planet. We all breathe the same air. We all cherish our children's future. And we are all mortal."

—JOHN F. KENNEDY, AMERICAN PRESIDENT

Whether you are skeptical of climate change or are a die-hard environmentalist, the global political community is moving in the direction of a Clean Revolution. After the signing of the Paris Climate Agreement, the global mindset has shifted to address carbon emissions, and the US can either be at the head of the table or leave the leadership to other countries, such as China. This Paris Climate Agreement is a clear market signal denoting where the market is moving. It's the acceleration of the Clean Revolution. The monumental agreement is a calling for innovation to this global problem.

THE PARIS CLIMATE AGREEMENT

On December 12, 2015, the historic Paris Climate Agreement was adopted by 196 nations across the globe with a target limiting carbon emissions in order to prevent global climate temperatures from rising more than 2°C. The 2°C target seems inconsequential, but the impacts of 2°C are massive. The best way to think about this is by comparing it to our own body temperature. The average body temperature is 98.6°F, but if you increased it 3.6°F (2°C), you're looking at 102.2°F, which is a fever and you're in bed. The earth's ecosystem is similar to our own bodily system, where a few degrees increase is the difference between normal and harmfully abnormal. Furthermore, fevers are usually caused by an infection, and the scientific community has a consensus that the "global fever" is being caused by carbon emissions. The world came together to work towards preventing the worst of a rising global fever.

At the center of the agreement was the United States and China, the two countries that accounted for 40 percent of global emissions.[1] After intense negotiations between Chinese and American officials, the symbolic agreement was a major win in collaboration for a global challenge between the leaders of the developing and developed worlds. Prior to the international meeting in Paris, the Executive Secretary of the UN Framework Convention on Climate Change, Christiana Figueres, was asked about the possibility of a global agreement, and she commented, "Not in my lifetime."[2] However, countries began to realize that addressing climate change was in their national and economic interest. An economic review of climate change shows that climate action cost 1 percent of GDP to transition to a clean economy, but climate inaction could cost 5–20 percent of GDP, depending on when we turn off the carbon faucet.[3]

As a part of the agreement, countries submitted strategies to cut their domestic emissions. The US pledged to reduce emissions by 26–28 percent by 2025 from 2005 levels, but since the agreement is voluntary, there are no penalties for nations that fail to achieve their targets. The agreement does not prescribe how to cut emissions. Instead it relies on the accountability among nations, which are scheduled to meet again in 2020 to discuss the progress on their emissions pledge.

The agreement also pledged for developed nations to contribute to the Green Climate Fund to help developing nations embrace a low-carbon economy while also adapting to the impacts of climate change. Developed nations agreed to contribute to this fund, with the understanding that developed economies have had the largest impact on cumulative atmospheric emissions over the past century. For example, even though the US only has 4 percent of the world's population, our nation is responsible for a third of the cumulative emissions in the atmosphere.[4] Emissions are a local issue that causes a global problem. Reducing emissions from developing nations will benefit the US, and vice versa. The problem is that developing nations don't have the infrastructure and funding resources at their disposal like the US does, which is why the Green Climate Fund is critical for moving the entire world toward a clean economy. The US pledged $1.0 billion per year over three years of the total $10.2 billion fund, which is pocket change compared to the annual federal budget of $4.0 trillion.[5]

President Trump views the Paris Climate Agreement as a financial disadvantage for America, but we need to change our lens to see it from a geopolitical perspective. Paying $3 billion is a small fee to be the leader at the global table for the transition of the global economy in the Clean Revolution. We should see the $3 billion as a membership fee to be a part of this multi-trillion dollar opportunity. Clean energy and clean mobility will continue to drop in price, and we will be in the backseat if we don't send the correct market signal to our American businesses. The Paris Climate Agreement is a call for American businesses to be a part of the Clean Revolution, and we are focusing backwards instead.

In our American past, conservative leaders have led environmental movements, such as conservation under Roosevelt, environmental policy under Nixon, and the Clean Air Act Amendments under Bush. Additionally, this was not the first time the global community has come together to address a global environmental crisis. In the late 1980s, scientists uncovered a growing hole in the ozone layer over Antarctica, which was discovered to be caused by man-made substances used for refrigeration, aerosols, air conditioning, and other appliances. The major signatories behind the agreement were conservative leaders: US President Ronald Reagan, Canadian Prime Minister Brian Mulroney, and UK Prime Minister Margaret Thatcher. Reagan sold US leadership for addressing this global issue as an "insurance policy," which, looking back retroactively, was a smart choice for America and for the globe. Addressing climate change is an insurance policy as well, as the cost of action is 1 percent of GDP while the cost of inaction could potentially be 5–20 percent of GDP.

"Thirty years ago the world proved it can come together and tackle a global problem with global resolve," said Erik

Solheim, head of the United Nations Environment Programme.[6] Due to international agreement, the ozone layer is on track to recovery over the next few decades.[7] Similar to the Montreal Protocol, our future depends on international cooperation with the Paris Climate Agreement. Unfortunately the tides have now turned on our path forward.

THE TRANSITION OF CLIMATE LEADERSHIP

"For us to join with the ranks of Syria and Nicaragua as being the only countries not to sign on this, I think is a mistake."

—REPRESENTATIVE FRED UPTON (R-MI), IN REGARD TO THE US WITHDRAWAL FROM THE PARIS CLIMATE AGREEMENT

On June 1, 2017, President Trump announced that he will withdraw from the Paris Climate Agreement in 2020, the earliest date to formally withdraw, arguing that it "is a massive redistribution of United States' wealth to other countries" and that "the American family will suffer the consequences in the form of lost jobs and a very diminished quality of life." Former Secretary of State Rex Tillerson, notably the former CEO of fossil fuel conglomerate Exxon Mobil, had previously advised the president to stay in the agreement, recognizing the importance of keeping America at head of the table.[8]

Trump famously said in his announcement: "I was elected to represent the citizens of Pittsburgh, not Paris."[9] Mayors, governors, faith-based groups, and business executives came out saying "We Are Still In," including the Mayor of Pittsburgh Bill Peduto himself. Pittsburgh Mayor Peduto responded via Twitter that "As the Mayor of Pittsburgh, I can assure you that we will follow the guidelines of the Paris Climate Agreement for our people, our economy & future."[10] The *Climate Mayors*, a bipartisan group of mayors focused on climate leadership, commented: "We will intensify efforts to meet each of our cities' current climate goals, push for new action to meet the 1.5 degrees Celsius target, and work together to create a twenty-first century clean energy economy."[11]

Criticism for the US withdrawal also came from Republican members of Congress, including Representative David Reichert (R-WA): "The Paris Accord gives the United States a global platform to be a leading voice on international issues impacting our economy, security, and the environment. Withdrawing from the agreement would cause us to lose this influence. I have always believed stewardship of our environment and sound economic policy are not mutually exclusive."[12]

In mid-2018, a China-EU Summit was held, where the two superpowers agreed to continue to cooperate on climate change and clean energy. The opening line in the joint statement from the Summit said: "The EU and China consider climate action and the clean energy transition an imperative more important than ever. They confirm their commitments under the historic 2015 Paris Agreement and step up their co-operation to enhance its implementation."[13]

With the US out, China is now in the driver's seat for climate leadership. Chinese President Xi Jinping commented, "Taking a driving seat in international cooperation to respond to climate change, China has become an important participant, contributor, and torchbearer in the global endeavor for ecological civilization."[14]

The world is moving forward toward a clean economy, with or without America. Right now, China is taking the reins of the inevitable Clean Industrial Revolution. It's time for American leadership to step up to the plate during this monumental time in history.

MISSION INNOVATION

"To be successful, you have to get the most out of the technology you already have while developing the technology you still need."

—BILL GATES, PHILANTHROPIST AND

FOUNDER OF MICROSOFT

At the same time the Paris Climate Agreement was signed, a new global initiative was announced, called the Mission Innovation (MI), where both the public sector and the private sector committed to increase global investment in clean energy research and development (R&D). The announcement included nineteen countries that committed to double their clean energy R&D over the following five years. On top of that, twenty-seven billionaire investors from ten countries committed to privately funding clean energy technologies as well, which is now called the Breakthrough Energy Ventures.

In 2015, global energy investments in R&D were approximately $15 billion, and twenty-three countries and the European Union have committed to this doubling of R&D spending, meaning a global investment of $30 billion by 2021.[15]

As a baseline in mid-2016, China had an R&D funding of $3.8 billion, while the US had $6.4 billion in funding. In a 2017 report, China has continued to commit to doubling its R&D funding to $7.6 billion, but once again, the US has decided to take a backseat in climate leadership by noting in the report that "The funding of energy-related research and development programs are currently under review by the new Administration."[16]

Fortunately, we still have private investments coming from the Breakthrough Energy Ventures. The billionaire coalition notes they are "investing in new technologies to find better, more efficient and cheaper energy sources" and are looking for investments in five key areas: electricity, transportation, agriculture, manufacturing, and buildings.[17] Investors include Microsoft founder Bill Gates, Virgin Group founder Richard Branson, Amazon founder Jeff Bezos, venture capitalist Vinod Khosla, and numerous other philanthropists. Investments in clean energy are not ideal for typical private investors, like venture capital (VC), because VC firms are typically looking at a return in five to ten years, whereas clean energy can take up to twenty years to come to fruition.[18] Building the next social media company is a much different feat than building a capital-intensive clean energy company. Funding from governments and long-term investors is required because of significant upfront capital and the longer time scale required for clean energy breakthroughs.

Despite the uncertainty behind US investments in clean energy R&D, the other countries that are part of Mission Innovation are moving full steam ahead, meaning the US is losing its competitive advantage, and we could soon be significantly behind. In the second half of the book, I go into detail about how the US can move significantly forward in innovation by enhancing investments in new clean technologies.

CLEAN ENERGY

As clean energy becomes more affordable and as nations move toward reducing their carbon emissions, some nations have already taken a big leap forward in transitioning to clean energy. Furthermore, multi-national corporations are also making "100% renewable energy" pledges, and a global shift is already happening in clean energy.

INTERNATIONAL ACTION

Costa Rica has been in the news the last several years, as the country was able to run off of 100 percent clean energy for 300 days in 2017. Additionally, from June 2014 until June 2018, Costa Rica generated 98.5 percent of its energy from clean energy: Hydroelectric (74 percent), Geothermal (11.9 percent), Wind (11.1 percent), Biomass (0.7 percent) and Solar (0.03 percent).[19] The country's constitution even had an amendment in 1994 that adds the right to a healthy environment for its citizens.[20]

The United Kingdom led the First Industrial Revolution with coal, but that story is changing in the Third Industrial Revolution. In 2008, the country committed to reducing emissions

80 percent by 2050 from 1990 levels. Since 2006, coal use has dropped 74 percent. Furthermore, on April 21, 2017, the UK went an entire day without coal use—the first time since the beginning of the First Industrial Revolution! On top of that, the country announced a commitment to close all remaining coal power plants by 2025.[21]

According to the International Energy Agency (IEA), the UK's grid was fueled by 24 percent by renewables and 19 percent by nuclear, meaning almost half of the UK was powered by clean electricity in 2016—with most of the remainder coming from natural gas.[22] Similar to China's present, the UK's past has had air quality problems from coal, which caused the "Great Smog of London." The UK was able to push cleaner energy sources as it implemented a price on carbon, where coal has twice the carbon emissions of natural gas.[23]

Not too far away, a similar story is happening in Germany, where the country is powered 30 percent by renewables and 13 percent by nuclear energy in 2016, where they are getting close to half of their energy production from clean energy. The country that is the reigning "King of Clean" is France, who is getting 73 percent of its energy from nuclear and 19 percent from renewables, for a whopping combination of 92 percent from clean energy.[24] France is also the largest exporter of electricity due to its cheap energy from nuclear to countries like Italy, the UK, Spain, Germany, and

Switzerland. The country made this strategic decision in 1974 after the global Oil Crisis of 1973 because France lacked domestic energy resources but had the engineering capabilities.[25] While decarbonization was not the prime motive of the French nuclear buildout, it is a good example of how motivated industrial policy can be effective.

Important to note, economic growth does not require growth in carbon emissions. Since 2000, the US has seen a 33 percent growth in GDP while seeing a 19 percent drop in carbon emissions.[26] We can continue to see economic growth without the need to pollute our skies and our communities.

CORPORATE ACTION

Governments aren't the only ones looking to clean up their energy supply, as multi-national companies are looking to do the same. In April 2018, Apple announced its global facilities were powered 100 percent by renewable energy, which includes offices, retail stores, and data centers in forty-three countries. Additionally, twenty-three of its suppliers had also committed to going to 100% renewable energy.

Apple's CEO Tim Cook commented, "We're committed to leaving the world better than we found it. After years of hard work we're proud to have reached this significant milestone."[27] Three months later, Apple announced a $300 million fund called the China Clean Energy Fund, which would jointly invest in one-gigawatt worth of clean energy projects for its suppliers, equivalent to powering a million homes.[28] Later that year in August, Apple became the first company to reach a $1 trillion dollar valuation, becoming the most valuable company in the world. So going clean does not mean losing "green."

If you think Apple is impressive, then check out Google, who also hit 100 percent in the same month as Apple. The company has contracts to purchase three gigawatts of renewable energy (compared to Apple's 0.5 GW for its own operations), which is equivalent to around $3 billion in new clean energy investments.[29]

It's not just tech companies going clean — AB InBev, the company responsible for the American classic Budweiser, also announced that the production of every single bottle of beer will be from 100 percent renewable energy by 2025 across the globe. In the US, all beer is already brewed with 100 percent renewable energy, and the company celebrated with the "100 percent Renewable Energy" logo on their Budweiser cans.[30]

There is even a global initiative dedicated to businesses that are going clean called RE100. Since the founding in 2014, 152 companies have committed to going to 100 percent renewable energy, including big names like IKEA, Bank of America, BMW, Coca Cola, Facebook, GM, Goldman Sachs, Lyft, Nike, Starbucks, and the list continues.[31]

The Clean Revolution isn't just happening with governments around the globe, it's happening with corporations around the globe as well.

CLEAN MOBILITY

Electric vehicles (EVs) are expected to grow from 3 millions cars on the road right now to 125 million by 2030, according to the International Energy Agency.[32] As EVs gain traction and as nations move toward reducing their carbon emissions, some nations have already taken a big leap forward in cleaning up their streets with drastic announcements such as bans on gas-powered vehicles. Furthermore, multi-national corporations are also embracing the movement to cleaner vehicles.

INTERNATIONAL ACTION

Numerous countries around the globe are calling for a ban on internal combustion engine (ICE) vehicles that are powered by fossil fuels. Both France and Britain are looking to ban ICE vehicle sales by 2040 while China is also looking at banning ICE vehicles, but has not yet put forward a timeline.[33,34]

Norway is leading the world in EV adoption, where 52 percent of new car sales were electric or hybrid in 2017, up from 40 percent in 2016. This is a big deal, considering that Norway is the second largest oil-producing country in Europe, only behind Russia. Ironically, oil and gas production has helped Norway build the world's largest sovereign wealth fund of $1 trillion, and now the country is pushing EV adoption by putting the right consumer incentives in place with financial exemptions: sales tax (~25 percent), registration tax (averages $12,000), parking fees, bridge and tunnel tolls, and ferry tickets.[35,36]

In China, smog covers the skies in major cities, so the country is trying to clean up its act and its air. In 2018, the city of Shenzhen announced that it has replaced its entire fleet of diesel buses with electric buses, the first major city in the world to do so. As a whole, Chinese cities are replacing 9,500 gas/diesel buses with electric buses every five weeks. To put it in perspective, LA has a bus fleet of 2,308, so China is replacing LA Metro's entire fleet four times over every five weeks.[37] According to a Bloomberg New Energy Finance report, electric buses are predicted to be nearly half of world's buses by 2025.[38] For every one thousand buses that China puts on the road, the country avoids importing five hundred barrels of oil a day, helping to put the country on a path to energy independence.[39]

CORPORATE ACTION

Auto manufacturers also have interest in electrifying their vehicles. Volvo announced in 2017 its plans to electrify all new models, with a mix of all-electric, plug-in hybrid, and traditional hybrid vehicles. Volvo CEO Håkan Samuelsson said, "We are determined to be the first premium car maker to move our entire portfolio of vehicles into electrification." Volvo delivered a half million vehicles in 2016, so it's able to make changes quicker than the bigger auto manufacturers like BMW and Mercedes-Benz, who sell over two million cars a year.[40]

Germany's BMW says twelve all-electric and thirteen hybrid car models will be on the market by 2025. Jaguar Land Rover announced all electric or hybrid models by 2020.[41] Over on this side of the pond, General Motors announced it would release twenty new all-electric vehicles by 2023. GM CEO Mary Barra said, "We have the ambition, the talent, and the technology to create a world with zero crashes, zero emissions, and zero congestion."[42]

Ridehailing services, like Uber, are also making pushes into electric vehicles. Uber announced a year-long pilot in 2018 to pay drivers additional revenue per trip for drivers who use EVs or plug-in hybrids. The company is testing it out in 7 cities, with Austin, Los Angeles, Montreal, Sacramento, San Diego, San Francisco, and Seattle.[43]

And cars aren't the only vehicles getting electrified. Tesla, the largest electric carmaker in the US, announced in late 2017 an electric semi-truck, and companies are already lining up with large orders: Anheuser-Busch (40), Walmart (45), Pepsi (100), UPS (125), and numerous other big brands.[44,45]

The mobility space will change quicker than many people believe, as the cost of batteries drop and the range of electric vehicles grow over time.

* * *

The Paris Climate Agreement has been signed, countries are embracing the Clean Revolution, and multi-national corporations are lining up to address this massive and growing market demand. The North Star of the international and business community is a transition to a clean economy. America needs to re-engage with the international community, and our American politicians need to give the correct market signals to ensure our country is the leader in this global movement. We can either continue our back-seat approach or become the driver of the world's greatest economic opportunity.

In the next several chapters, I will discuss how China has supported its domestic energy and mobility markets with its current and future plans to expand internationally. "Support local and then grow global" is the strategy being embraced by China, and the US needs to do the same if we want to be a leader in the next Industrial Revolution.

CHAPTER 3

CHINA'S GLOBAL AMBITIONS

———

"The Chinese people are a great people; they are industrious and brave, and they never pause in pursuit of progress."

—XI JINPING, CHINESE PRESIDENT

China is currently ahead of the US in the Clean Revolution, but the average American isn't following the transition that is underway in China, including me before I began writing this book. When you think of "Made in China," you may think of low-quality products and mass manufacturing. However, China is investing heavily to innovate into more advanced manufacturing, and the country is aiming to dominate world trade through its Belt and Road Initiative – the biggest global infrastructure project in history. American politicians and the media have been discussing jobs being lost to China, but we should expect that trend to accelerate as China aims to become the dominant manufacturer for the entire world.

China is entering an aggressive transition from *imitation* to *innovation*, which is driven by a mix of domestic and global ambitions. The stereotype is that Chinese industries imitate (or steal) other innovative technologies, but the Chinese landscape is quickly changing, as the country seeks to be a world leader in technology. As George Yip, author of *China's Next Strategic Advantage: From Imitation to Innovation*, put it: "[China has] actually a very rare trifecta…a triple play of a large home market, scientific and engineering capability, and manufacturing capability."[1] These advantages will help China for its aggressive moves to be an industry leader in cleantech.

INCENTIVES TO LEAD THE CLEAN REVOLUTION

China has a clear understanding of why they need to move forward and lead this Clean Revolution. There are clear political, geopolitical, and economic incentives to be at the head of the table for both innovation and global leadership.

Political Incentive: As China continues to grow its economy, it needs more and more energy, which is greatly fueled by coal at this time. The vast number of coal plants and the sea of gas-powered vehicles have led to significant air quality issues in many cities, especially in China's capital Beijing, leading to what has been called the "Airpocalypse."[2] According to a report from University of California at Berkeley, 1.6 million people die in China each year from heart, lung, and stroke problems stemming from pollution and air quality issues.[3] President Xi is implementing measures to address the air quality issues, with the unspoken reason that unhappy citizens could lead to social unrest and problems for the political party short term and long term. The country has gone as far as to block web access to the documentary *Under the Dome*, a film that criticized China's pollution problem and received hundreds of millions of views on Chinese websites.[4] Air pollution poses a threat to the Community Party of China.

Geopolitical Incentive: As China's demand for energy grows, the country wants to become self-sufficient for energy sources in the long term. For example, a push into electric vehicles would decrease China's dependence on foreign countries for fossil fuels. During geopolitical negotiations, leverage is important. That's why self-sufficiency is a strategic advantage for China, as its global ambitions grow over the next few decades. As I will discuss later, China's Belt and Road Initiative is similar to the Marshall Plan, where China provides financing for infrastructure, which is helping the country to build strategic allies across the globe.

Economic Incentive: The world has now signed the Paris Climate Agreement, so the globe is moving toward a sustainable and clean future. The writing is on the wall, and China can sell cleantech innovation to nations around the world who are looking to cut emissions. A select number of countries have the manufacturing and innovation capabilities to lead the cleantech movement, and China sees the dollar signs from the entire world transitioning their entire energy and mobility sectors, worth trillions of dollars. The Organisation for Economic Co-operation and Development (OECD) notes that to keep global warming to 2°C, a global investment of $6.9 trillion in infrastructure is needed <u>per year</u>, which is a major economic opportunity for the innovative countries and companies that lead this transition.[5]

China has the ability to clean up their air, remove their foreign dependence on fossil fuels, and be the global innovator for cleantech around the world. Moving away from fossil fuels and investing in cleantech innovation is a clear win-win-win situation for China. Their global ambitions will help them take a strategic role in clean energy and clean mobility as well.

2025 & 2049

Over the next thirty years, China is planning to disrupt the global marketplace and geopolitical leadership with two key target dates — 2025 and 2049. When President Xi took office, he declared "the greatest Chinese dream is the great rejuvenation of the Chinese nation."[6]

MADE IN CHINA 2025

In 2015, China released an ambitious blueprint to enhance their role in advanced manufacturing, with a key purpose of creating higher-paying jobs similar to other developed countries. China is mirroring Germany's "Industry 4.0," which ultimately applies information technology (IT) to manufacturing. Think of the Internet of Things (IoT) meets manufacturing and logistics. It's an expansive plan to compete with the big dogs, like the US, Germany, and Japan.

China has taken a lot of America's low-quality labor-intensive manufacturing jobs, but they are now gunning for our advanced tech industries as well. The plan discusses "self-sufficiency," so in the short term, China will be a competitor, but in the long term, they plan for most of their manufacturing to be home grown, rather than rely on countries like the US, Germany, and South Korea. Lorand Laskai at the Council on Foreign Relations put it well: "In the saga of the U.S.--China economic rivalry, Made in China 2025 is shaping up to be the central villain, the real existential threat to U.S. technological leadership."[7]

Here are the top ten priority sectors that China wants to dominate:

1. New advanced information technology
2. Automated machine tools and robotics
3. Aerospace and aeronautical equipment
4. Maritime equipment and high-tech shipping
5. Modern rail transport equipment
6. **New-energy vehicles**
7. **Energy equipment**
8. Agricultural equipment
9. New materials
10. Biopharma and advanced medical products[8]

Related to this theme of the ongoing Clean Revolution, two of the ten priorities are related to addressing climate change and becoming a cleantech "powerhouse" (no pun intended). In the next few chapters, we will take a deep dive into China's ambitions for electric vehicles and clean energy.

The reason for this strategic economic transition is that wages increase as advanced manufacturing becomes more prominent, so China wants to overcome the "middle-income trap," where a country's growth slows after achieving middle incomes. Of the 101 "middle-income economies" in the 1960s, only thirteen have become "high-income economies" by 2008.[9] In the US, we constantly talk about China taking away low-paying manufacturing jobs. Well, they are also coming for our high-paying jobs as a part of this 2025 initiative.

This aggressive manufacturing plan poses a big threat to American industries, evident by President Trump's imposed tariffs on China in the second half of 2018. Beijing has now started downplaying the initiative, as the reports have noted that "Made in China 2025" had been mentioned 140 times in the first five months of 2018 on the state news agency Xinhua, but since June 5, no mentions have been reported.[10]

2049

"Made in China 2025" is the first step in the process to catch up to other developed nations in industrial prowess. The ultimate goal is to become a dominant player in the world market by 2049, the 100th anniversary of the People's Republic of China. This is ultimately President Xi's vision to become a global superpower by 2049. 2025 and 2049 are not only about economic growth, as it is much more, noted by President Xi comment that "only by firmly grasping key core technology in our hands can we fundamentally guarantee national economic security, national defense, and other security."[11]

The country has a strategy behind this ambitious plan as well. Here is how China is making great strides:

- **Targets**: China has put forward public goals and also behind-the-scene goals, so that private and public firms can adjust their business plans toward the country's goals. This is in stark contrast to the US, which has very little vision for the future of where the country and its industries are going. In the US, some of the departments and agencies of the executive branch put out goals, but those goals change suddenly as new administrations take over. Priorities in the Environmental Protection Agency in particular have reversed from the Obama administration to the Trump administration. China's national strategic goals have a big advantage in directing the flock of birds in a single direction.

- **Subsidies**: China supports industries by providing state funding, tax breaks, low-interest loans, and other subsidies. China views these investments in industry as investing in China's future. Some American leaders believe in a free market, where government shouldn't pick today's winners and losers. China is doing the opposite. Their government is looking at the *future* and determining which technologies will be the innovation of tomorrow. For example, China knows that pollution and emissions are growing current and future problems, so they are purposely supporting the electric vehicle industry, which will we discuss more in the following chapters. In the next decade, when US manufacturers are catching up to the innovation curve, China will be years and years ahead in EV technology. The trick is to subsidize innovative industries until they are mature. It's not about picking the current winners and losers – it's about placing bets on the future winners.

- **Foreign Investments**: Both private and state-backed companies are involved with a great amount of foreign investments and acquisitions around the globe. Instead of spending money on R&D, you can just buy the technology from foreign companies. US acquisitions by Chinese companies peaked in 2016 with a value of $45 billion. Congress has become so worried about Chinese investments that over the last several years, legislation has passed to expand the duties and staffing for the Committee on Foreign Investment in the United States (CFIUS), which is an interagency panel that reviews foreign transactions for potential security risks. In 2018, the Foreign Investment Risk Review Modernization Act (FIRRMA) was enacted, which is the largest reform for CFIUS in two decades. One of the authors of the bill Senator John Cornyn (R-TX) said "China has weaponized investment in an attempt to vacuum up our advanced technologies."[12] It's also important to remember that many investments could come from state-owned enterprises (SOEs), which account for a third of China's GDP, yet two-thirds of foreign investments.

- **Joint Ventures**: China requires foreign businesses that want to do business in the country to do so through joint ventures (JVs) with domestic Chinese businesses. The key problem with this is the potential for Chinese businesses to access intellectual property and proprietary industrial processes. For example, China requires auto manufacturers to partner with domestic auto or battery companies, in order to do business in China.[13] However, most recently, China is potentially becoming more relaxed. Tesla will be the first car company to avoid a JV with its new manufacturing facility in Shanghai[14], which fits nicely with the electric vehicle priority for Made in China 2025.

Because of China's national strategy behind 2025 and 2049, the US should wake up to the ambitious plans to become the next top global superpower.

THE BELT AND ROAD INITIATIVE

If China aims to become an industrial powerhouse, the country will need to be able to easily move their goods around the globe, including clean energy and electric vehicles. China is on top of it with its the Belt and Road Initiative—the biggest global infrastructure project in history. To understand this project, you have to take a step back into ancient times with the Silk Road, which connected Asia to Africa and Europe. The road was named after the lucrative trade of silk that came out of China although other goods and ideas were also spread along these terrestrial and maritime routes. A German geographer Ferdinand von Richthofen who traveled to China from 1868 to 1872 on seven expeditions coined the term "Silk Road".

China has now revised the ancient Silk Road into the modern-day Belt and Road Initiative (BRI) to enhance connectivity and cooperation between Eurasian countries. The "Belt" refers to the terrestrial interconnected corridors while the "Road" refers to the maritime corridors. In the bordering country Kazakhstan, President Xi said, "We should take an innovative approach and jointly build an Economic Belt along the Silk Road."

Again, across the South China Sea in Indonesia, he repeats, "The two sides should work together to build up a new Maritime Silk Road in the twenty-first century." China is spending around $150 billion per year for the sixty-eight countries interested in funding infrastructure projects. China's Foreign Minister Wang Yi notes that BRI is President Xi's most important foreign policy. China wants to be the dominant country for trade in Eurasia, just as the US is for the Americas.[15] By improving trade connectivity in the region, China can cut trade costs and increase trade with other Eurasian countries, which account for 30 percent of global GDP, 62 percent of global population, and 75 percent of known energy reserves.[16]

The plans for the Economic Belt contain six on-land corridors taking goods in and out of China, while the Maritime Silk Road is a chain of seaports directing trade in and out of China. A great example is a new port in Gwadar, Pakistan.

Very few industries wanted to invest in Pakistan due to its collapsing economy. On top of that, there was a highway and railway connecting the port to China, which was a $62 billion project. It not only benefited China to easily trade goods across several continents, but it also created an alternative pathway for oil and gas from the Middle East, which is a major win for China's energy security.

But there could be another reason why China is providing these infrastructure loans to countries. "John Adams said infamously that a way to subjugate a country is through either the sword or debt. China has chosen the latter," said Brahma Chellaney, an analyst at a New Delhi think tank, in an article with *The New York Times*. He was referring to what happened in Sri Lanka at a port financed by China. President Mahinda Rajapaksa, who gained control of Sri Lanka's government in 2005, wanted to build a port in his home district of Hambantota, yet feasibility studies showed that the small country did not need to expand beyond the country's existing port. Other lenders, such as neighboring country India, said no to the funding requests because it did not make economic sense.

As a part of the deal with China, Sri Lanka's government was required to use one of Beijing's largest state-owned enterprises, China Harbor Engineering Company, rather than an open bid process. Checks also began to flow into Mr.

Rajapaksa's 2015 presidential campaign. Eventually Rajapaksa was voted out of office, but the country was still stuck with a tremendous amount of debt to China. Eventually to cut down debt, Sri Lanka leased the port to China for 99 years, giving China a strategic stronghold off the shoreline of India.[17] Having access to strategic alliances and ports will cause geopolitical challenges in the future, as we saw in America's past with issues in Cuba with the Soviet Union.

International response to the BRI has been negative as well. In mid-2018, thirty-seven EU ambassadors compiled a report that highly criticized China's efforts, noting that their actions are hampering free trade and putting the Chinese industry at an advantage. The CEO of Siemens said that "China's 'One Belt, One Road' will be the new World Trade Organization whether we like it or not," while speaking at the World Economic Forum in early 2018.[18] The BRI could be seen as the modern-day Marshall Plan, as China forms strategic allies through financial means. As it lays the physical and financial groundwork around the world, it will be easier for China to provide clean energy and electric vehicles to markets around the world.

PLANNING FOR THE FUTURE

China is able to make such long-term economic plays because they actually plan for it, which is why the country has made significant progress in economic growth in the last several decades. China purposely has ambitious and strategic planning with what they call their *Five-Year Plans*. The first plan began in 1953, and most recently there has been the Twelfth Plan (2011–2015) and Thirteenth Plan (2016–2020).

The Five-Year Plans range from economic goals to improving social issues. In the previous Twelfth Plan, China aimed to grow GDP by 8 percent, achieve 7 percent growth of per capita income per year, and fund 2.2 percent of GDP on research and development. It also looked at increasing anti-corruption efforts, fixing the rising cost of housing, and readjusting income distribution. In the Thirteenth Plan that is currently underway, China has a long list of plans, including changing the one-child policy to a two-child policy and the previously discussed Made in China 2025 initiative.

In the Thirteenth Plan, a few relevant policies for our discussion are:

- **Audits**: "Audit systems proposed for officials who leave their current posts, taking environmental protection into consideration. Officials' efforts to protect natural resources to form part of their performance appraisal."

- **Energy**: "Clean production to be promoted and green/low-carbon industry systems set up."

- **Mobility**: "Use of new energy vehicles to be promoted and the industrialization level of electric cars improved."

- **Finance**: "Green finance to be promoted and a green development fund established."[19]

I wanted to begin with the audit systems because it is such a different idea than how the American government is structured. China has a very top-down approach with government, so audits are ultimately like an exit interview that companies sometimes hold when you leave a job. Except this is for government officials all around China, and part of their review includes environmental protection.

According to the National Audit Office, more than 1,200 Chinese officials have been audited, and the audits would impact future promotions.[20,21] Imagine if US members of Congress, Governors, and Mayors got an audit on the way out regarding their actions on environmental issues. That would never happen in the US, but if it did, I'm sure we'd have a totally different conversation around the environment today. When Chinese officials around the country are making important political decisions, they know the environmental impact of their decision will be taken into account. Environmental accountability will play a big role for Chinese officials at every level of government.

In the next chapters, we will discuss how China is innovating in energy and mobility, so we will get a better understanding of China's big support and investments in these two important sectors.

Lastly, China has also been supportive of cleantech by implementing policies around "green finance," which is supported by the Green Finance Committee of China Society for Finance and Banking. In 2016, China became the largest issuer of green bonds with a total value of $34 billion, accounting for 40 percent of global green bonds, which are going toward clean energy projects around the country. Green bonds are important because they bring in domestic and international money. China has also seen two hundred and fifty green investment funds launched, consisting of fifty local public funds and two hundred private sector funds, as well as launching eighteen green equity and bond indices on the Chinese stock exchanges.[22] Beyond local investments, China could also look to invest in clean energy infrastructure projects in developing countries built and financed by China.

SCIENCE AND TECHNOLOGY

Over the last decade, China has made a major push into science and technology, as it recognizes the major economic benefits. In 2006, China launched its fifteen-year

"Medium- to Long-Term Plan for the Development of Science and Technology" (abbreviated as MLP), which calls for China to be an "innovation-oriented society" by 2020 and a world leader in science and technology (S&T) by 2050.

CHINA'S S&T GOALS BY 2020	
FOUR TARGETS	**FIVE STRATEGIC FOCUSES**
Invest 2.5% of GDP in R&D	Develop technologies in energy, water resources and environmental protection
Reduce China's dependence on foreign technologies to 30%	Provide innovation in IT and new materials to improve China's technologies in manufacturing
Increase the contribution of technologies to economic growth to 60%	Develop biotechnology to further its application in agriculture, industry, human and health services
Rank in the world's top five countries in patents granted and citations used in international science paper	Accelerate the development of aerospace and marine technology
	Strengthen R&D in basic science and cutting-edge technology

Source: China Ministry of Science and Technology[23]

Notably, the one of the strategic focuses is to develop technologies in energy and environmental protection. The plan also had a list of the top twenty strategic research topics, which included (1) Ecology, environmental protection, and recycled economy S&T, (2) Energy, resources, and ocean S&T, and (3) Transportation S&T.

Over the last three decades, China has significantly ramped its investments in research and development, which has grown from 0.56 percent of GDP in 1996 to 2.1 percent by 2015. In comparison, the US still leads with 2.8 percent of GDP going toward R&D in 2015.

R&D EXPENDITURE, AS A PERCENTAGE OF GDP

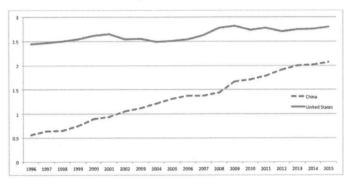

Source: The World Bank's DataBank[24]

R&D dollars are important for the energy of tomorrow, but China has also been putting a lot of money in renewable energy investments for the technologies of today. As noted below, China outspent the US in new renewable energy investments three-to-one. Even though China is the biggest carbon emitter in the world, China is also the largest clean energy investor in the world.

NEW RENEWABLE ENERGY INVESTMENTS
– TOP 10 COUNTRIES (IN $ BILLIONS)

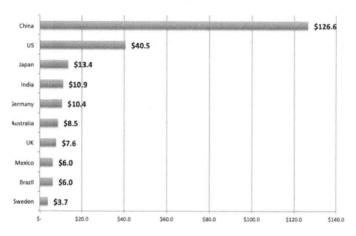

Source: *The Atlas – "Global Trends in Renewable Energy Investments 2018"*[25]

* * *

Over the last several decades, China has made several strategies to bring it to the forefront of innovation. With Made in China 2025, President Xi is setting up China to become a dominant player in advanced manufacturing, competing with the top manufacturing powerhouses, like the US. Of the top ten industries that China is focusing on, new energy vehicles and clean energy are on the list. Furthermore, China's Belt and Road Initiative is interconnecting Eurasia in order for China to dominate the future of global trade through finance and infrastructure. BRI will play a major role in the

Clean Revolution to help China sell clean energy projects and electric vehicles to both developing and developed countries around the globe. In the next two chapters, we dive deeper into the technologies that are becoming more prominent in China around clean energy and clean mobility.

KEY TAKEAWAYS

- **Made in China 2025**: President Xi is pushing China into more advanced manufacturing through its Made in China 2025 initiative, which is focused on ten key industries, including new energy vehicles and clean energy. In the next two chapters, we will discuss how this plan is already paying off in these two cleantech sectors.

- **Belt and Road Initiative**: China is re-birthing the Silk Road by interconnecting Eurasia, helping the country to become a global trade superpower. BRI is the modern-day Marshall Plan, where China is building strategic allies through finance and infrastructure. These strategic allies are already leading to clean energy projects around the globe, which we will discuss in the next chapter.

- **Science and Technology**: China is transitioning from imitation to innovation, as the country has drastically increased its domestic R&D funding. Even though China is the biggest emitter, the country is also the biggest investor in cleantech investments, setting the country up for success in the Clean Revolution.

"When I was growing up, my parents told me, 'Finish your dinner. People in China and India are starving.' I tell my daughters, 'Finish your homework. People in India and China are starving for your job.'"

—THOMAS FRIEDMAN, AMERICAN

JOURNALIST AND AUTHOR

CHAPTER 4

CHINA'S DISRUPTION IN CLEAN ENERGY

———

"China highly values clean energy development and has taken a series of measures and achieved positive outcomes in this area."

—XI JINPING, CHINESE PRESIDENT

America's biggest iconic brands—like Apple, GM, and Tesla—recognize the importance of the Chinese market and the country's desire to transition to the next Clean Industrial Revolution. In mid-2018, Apple announced a clean energy fund in China to help suppliers in its supply chain go 100 percent renewable energy, with a commitment of $300 million investment over four years. In 2019, Tesla is expected to begin operations at its new Shanghai factory in order to reduce transport costs and tariffs for the world's largest EV market.[1] General Motors CEO was initially against China's announced ban on gas-powered cars, but the American automaker is now on board with an "all-electric future."[2] China's ambitious goals for a clean future are even pushing iconic American brands to make significant investments in the Clean Revolution, particularly in China.

CLEAN ENERGY

China has a giant lead in the clean revolution, as 60 percent of global solar cells are manufactured by Chinese companies. Furthermore, US advanced nuclear companies are looking to China for being a test bed. TerraPower, an advanced nuclear company funded by Bill Gates, planned to test out its next-generation nuclear reactor in the Chinese city of Cangzhou, but the trade war has ended this endeavor. The American company "found it remarkably challenging to build or secure access to the range of equipment, materials, and technology required to successfully commercialize its innovative design" in the US, and so it looked abroad for more innovative countries as a testbed, such as China in this case.[3] This should be a Sputnik moment for America, so we can support American entrepreneurs and scientists.

A goal is a just dream until you put a deadline on it. China began its clean energy revolution with the passage of the

Renewable Energy Law in 2005, which prioritized the development and usage of renewable energy. In late 2018, China announced that it would be increasing its Renewable Portfolio Standard (RPS) to 35 percent renewable energy by 2030 from the previous target of 20 percent "non-fossil fuels" energy. The strategic move aims to remove the country's reliance on coal and would put fines on noncompliant companies, to be used for renewable projects.[4] The EU has a target of 40 percent renewables by 2030. The US doesn't have a national RPS, as energy goals occur at the state level. California has pledged 50 percent renewables by 2030 and 100 percent "clean" electricity by 2045, and Hawaii has pledged to 100 percent by 2045. A majority of states do not have an RPS, however.

We could also see China's share of renewable generation grow as the country addresses curtailment, meaning solar and wind were in place and producing power, but other sources of energy were taking priority on the grid. These happen for two reasons: grid operators will prioritize certain resources in some regions, or some projects aren't yet connected to the grid. Nationally, curtailment rates can be as high as 15–20 percent in 2015/2016, but by 2017 curtailment rates were 12 percent for wind and 6 percent for solar. As China addresses these issues, we could see the renewable share of electricity climb.

Thinking more globally, China's largest grid operator State Grid Corporation of China ("State Grid") also has a vision for a worldwide interconnected grid, called the Global Energy Interconnection (GEI). GEI would be a combination of an ultra-high voltage grid as a part of a smart grid powered by renewable energy.

The President of State Grid Liu Zhenya made an analogy of the vision: "The Internet is like the nervous system, while electric grids are like the blood vessels. As the nervous system is interconnected, so must the blood system be." The timelines of this vision include: *2030* when all countries and continents will be interconnected, and *2050* when 80 percent of the grid will be powered by renewable energy.

President Xi presented the plan for a global grid at the United Nations in 2015, and in response Georg Kell, founding executive director of United Nations Global Compact, commented: "It is without doubt one of the most important initiatives ever. It will not only make a major contribution to the reduction of emissions that cause global warming and toxic air pollution, but it will also provide for access to energy and thus support advanced sustainable development."[5]

SOLAR

In 2017, China accounted for 50 percent of worldwide solar demand. As a nation, China is way ahead of its targets for solar power generation. As a part of its Thirteenth Five-Year

Plan (2016-2020), the country aimed for a national target of 105 GW for installed capacity, but had already reached 150 GW in the second half of 2018—far ahead of schedule. This is massive growth, as China had cumulative solar installation of only 2.5 GW in 2011.[6]

As previously mentioned, China is responsible for 60 percent of the global market for manufactured solar cells. The reason is that China was able to drop the price of solar panels by 80 percent between 2008 and 2013—the US invented the technology, but China made it affordable. China first got a wave of solar manufacturers due to the country's interest in solar for domestic use. At the same time in the late 1990s, Germany incentivized and therefore increased demand for solar energy development. German manufacturers couldn't meet the full demand for solar, so China noticed the export opportunities of solar panels to Germany. By the mid-2000s, a second wave of Chinese solar manufacturers entered to address Germany's demand, with the added bonus of financial support from state-owned, provincial, and municipal financial institutions. In the late 2000s, the Chinese Development Bank made $47 billion in credit facilities for both solar and wind manufacturers, and by 2011, China was responsible for 46 percent of the global supply of solar modules.[7]

The governmental support of Chinese solar manufacturers allowed China to become a global solar powerhouse within a little over a decade. The biggest solar manufacturers in China now are Trina Solar, Yingli Solar, JinkoSolar, Suntech Solar, and JA Solar.[8] On the top ten list of global manufacturers, Chinese companies hold seven out of the spots, with no American companies found on the list.[9]

As mentioned in the book introduction, one of the first industries President Trump waged a trade war with was solar modules and panels from China. Over the past six years, US manufacturers have closed over a dozen manufacturing plants across the US. The 30 percent tariff on imported solar panels sounds like a great way to incentivize American manufacturing of solar panels, but most jobs in the industry actually come from solar installation, with 38,000 working in manufacturing out of the total 260,000–370,000 of broad solar jobs.

Little positive news has come out of the efforts, except for a manufacturing plant investment from Chinese firm JinkoSolar, which is only expected to add 200 jobs.[10] It's believed that the increased costs on solar projects will outweigh the added jobs in the manufacturing.[11] In the end, Chinese firms may take a financial hit, but here in America, consumers of rooftop solar and developers of solar projects will also see a financial hit.

With solar, China has shown how government support of winners can led to major economic opportunities around the world. China's energy dominance will continue as countries around the world work to clean up their electric grid with clean energy like solar.

WIND

Solar isn't the only area where China is a key "powerhouse." China leads the world in wind deployment, accounting for nearly one-third of global wind capacity.[12] Between 2007 and 2011, China had installed more wind capacity than the US or Germany in over thirty years of wind development.

China had its first wind farm demonstration in 1986, and the Chinese industry started to develop slowly in the late 1990s with more small-scale wind turbines. The development was able to occur because the former Ministry of Electric Power called for wind farms to be connected to the grid and that all electric production be purchased, which led to loan investments due to financial security of the farms.

China's State Planning Commission (SPC) added extra benefits to wind investors by extending loan payments to fifteen years and cutting the Value Added Tax in half (to 8.5 percent). By 1997, SPC launched a new initiative "Ride the Wind Programme" to develop 1 GW of wind power by 2001, which led to joint ventures to develop wind projects between a local Chinese company and a foreign wind developer.

The Chinese wind industry really took off when the National Development and Reform Commission (NDRC) added competitive bidding and localization requirements for wind projects, meaning that companies had to submit bids for wind projects and 70 percent of the projects had to be domestically produced, incentivizing foreign companies to set up manufacturing plants in China. The impact of large wind firms meant that the cost to manufacture and procure wind energy would come down over time. In 2008, China launched the Wind Base Programme with the goal of achieving 10 GW of wind by 2020 in seven selected wind-rich regions.

China was able to cover the cost of the new wind projects and reimburse wind projects for their electricity production (known as a feed-in tariff) by adding a small surcharge on electricity prices. China also began fixing issues between the electricity sector and transmission planning by strengthening coordination for grid interconnection of wind projects.[13]

From the thirty years of China's wind policy, the country was able to make significant progress domestically through the national efforts: aggressive wind energy targets, pre-determined wind-rich zones, feed-in tariffs, priority access to the grid, interconnection coordination, competitive bidding, and localization (70 percent local production). Both state-owned and private enterprises competed the same as they would in a capitalist market, but the growth of the domestic wind industry wouldn't have thrived without the national industry-friendly policies in place to make investments in wind power successful for investors and companies.

Today, China has some of the largest wind turbines manufacturers, including Goldwind, United Power, and Envision Energy. Of the top ten wind manufacturers worldwide in 2017, Chinese companies accounted for three on the list while the American companies accounted for just one (General Electric).[14] Goldwind has subsidiaries around the world, including Goldwind Americas, where the manufacturer and developer is doing projects in states like Texas, the heartland of American fossil fuels. Ohio is another place where Goldwind has projects going to supply energy to Whirlpool Corporation at their facilities in Marion and Ottawa.

CEO Jereme Kent of One Energy Enterprises, the managing company of these projects, stated: "Manufacturers are taking control of their energy future. They want clean energy, they want low fixed rates, and they want it now; and that is exactly what we give them. Goldwind has earned their seat at the table for this emerging Commercial & Industrial (C&I) market over the last five years."[15]

Similar to the story with solar, the wind industry has also seen impacts from the trade war with China. Tom Kiernan, the CEO of the American Wind Energy Association, said that tariffs on imports, with steel in particular, could lead to a 10 percent increase in the cost of wind energy in the US.[16]

Just like solar, the increased costs in wind energy will likely outweigh the benefits of potentially increased manufacturing capabilities. The US could learn from China by supporting the wind industry through effective and industry-friendly policies, rather than putting higher prices on imported goods that ultimately hurt the end-consumers, such as American citizens and businesses through higher energy prices.

HYDRO

Similar to wind and solar energy, China also leads the world in hydropower development, with three times the capacity of any other nation. In 2017, China constructed 9 GW of new hydropower capacity, accounting for 40 percent of the global new construction. By 2021, the Asian powerhouse will account for a third of new global capacity.

China has the world's largest hydropower dam called Three Gorges Dam, which became fully operational in 2012 and is responsible for 22.5 GW of capacity. Planning for the dam (and hydropower in general) began in 1980s, and development grew steadily through the 1990s and 2000s. The Twelfth Five-Year Plan (2011-2015) called for a 30 percent growth in hydro, from 200 GW to 260 GW of capacity, but China significantly bypassed that target with 319 GW by 2015. In the Thirteenth Five-Year Plan (2016-2020), China is now aiming for 380 GW by 2020 and 470 GW by 2025. NDRC is also researching pumped hydro, where plants can pump water back up to higher elevations to "store" energy for later use, which will play a significant role in balancing the grid for China's ambitious plans for solar and wind projects.[17]

Hydropower has been a strategic priority for China since the country has vast mountains and rivers to run hydropower dams. In the last two decades, international focus has also been a major focus for Chinese hydro manufacturers as a part of China's 1999 "Going Out" policy, influencing domestic companies to compete for international projects.

China's largest hydropower company PowerChina Resources is estimated to have 50 percent of the international hydro construction market, after merging with Sinhydro in 2011.[18] China has been doing significant work with financing and building hydropower in Latin American countries, including Argentina, Belize, Bolivia, Brazil, Colombia, Costa Rica, Ecuador, Guyana, Honduras, Peru, and Venezuela.[19]

China's push into hydropower has helped to spur this clean energy source, with an initial growth domestically and then eventually to the rest of the globe.

NUCLEAR

Nuclear plays an important role in China's energy grid because solar and wind projects tend to be built in remote areas, whereas nuclear power can be built closer to population-dense cities. Currently China has forty-five nuclear plants in operation, fifteen under construction, and more in the planning phase. In the Thirteenth Five-Year Plan (2016–2020), the country is looking to approve six to eight nuclear reactors each year, with a target of 58 GW of nuclear by 2020, with 30 GW under construction. In late 2018, the NDRC's Energy Research Institute commented that China must increase nuclear capacity by 554 GW by 2050 if the country is going to help limit global warming under 1.5°C, meaning a nuclear energy share from 4 percent to 28 percent. In comparison, 20 percent of the US power mix comes from nuclear, but much of America's nuclear plants are reaching near the end of their lifetime, and current constructions are seeing significant delays and budget issues.[20]

Outside of China, global nuclear generation has seen declines over the last several years due to issues with Fukushima and construction costs, while China is moving in the opposite direction by ramping up nuclear energy. Fukushima should be a warning to assess operational issues with dated nuclear reactors, but it shouldn't stop the world from exploring next generation nuclear technologies. As I stated in the introduction, problems should be seen as opportunities, and China is seeing the opportunity to become a world leader in nuclear power as many countries are backing away.

As carbon emission reduction becomes a bigger and bigger priority over the next few decades, the international community will be looking for quick ways to cut emissions, and next-gen nuclear will be a rapid solution with large-scale projects. As another lesson, many antiquated nuclear technologies rely on a continuous water supply to cool the reactor, so many nuclear disasters have occurred due to water supply issues, leading to the rare meltdowns.

Next-gen nuclear relies on completely different processes, with most not needing a constant water supply. Waterless nuclear technologies will also become more important in the energy mix, as water drought issues become more prominent with global warming. Coal, natural gas, and legacy nuclear plants rely on water supply, whereas solar, wind, and next-gen nuclear can be built anywhere.

Cost over time will also be a driving factor in nuclear development. An MIT study found that reactors in China, Korea, and the UAE (being heavily built by Koreans) cost $3,000–$4,000 per kilowatt, whereas in the West, nuclear costs are over $8,000 per kilowatt—nearly two times higher![21] As China grows its domestic market for nuclear, it could continue to drive down the cost of nuclear plants, which will lead to more nuclear development around world from Chinese companies, such as The China National Nuclear Corporation (GNC) and China General Nuclear Power Group (CGN).

TOTAL CAPITAL COSTS FOR HISTORICAL AND ONGOING NUCLEAR PROJECTS

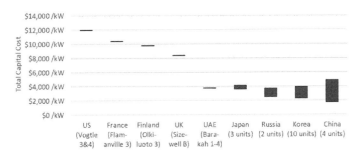

Source: The ETI Nuclear Cost Drivers Project, Summary Report (April 2018)[22]

Internationally, China is already looking to explore opportunities for its third-generation nuclear reactor, called the Hualong One, to other markets, evident by investments by Chinese companies in the UK. CGN is partnering with French company Électricité de France (EDF) to construct a new nuclear plant using the Hualong One reactor technology in the UK, which could help China build a track record in the UK and later expand to other European countries. Prime Minister Theresa May delayed initial approval to the Hinkley Point nuclear plant due to security concerns with a Chinese state-owned company having 30 percent control over major infrastructure projects, but the deal was later approved in 2016.

Furthermore, British company Centrica is looking to sell its 20 percent stake in eight nuclear plants, and CGN is interested in the investment.[23] One worry for the UK could be that the state-owned company puts in a "backdoor system" to threaten shutting down nuclear capacity in future diplomatic negotiations.[24] The Atlantic Council, an American think tank on international affairs, put out a report discussing the need for the US to re-engage with nuclear energy leadership, as China and Russia have now taken an international focus on building nuclear plants, especially in strategic regions for the US in the Middle East and South Asia. The report concluded that "US global nuclear engagement is critical—not only because it supports military needs and advances commercial interests, but also because it brings with it a culture that promotes safety, security of nuclear materials, and nonproliferation."[25] China's global nuclear ambitions could play a critical role in both reducing carbon emissions and having leverage in geopolitical discussions.

China isn't only focusing on nuclear fission, the typical technology when people talk about "nuclear energy," but also exploring and investing in two other important nuclear technologies: nuclear fusion and thorium.

First, with nuclear fusion, in late 2018, Chinese researchers hit a major milestone by hitting one hundred million degrees Celsius, which uses the same energy process as our sun. China constructed the Experimental Advanced Superconducting Tokamak (known as "EAST") in 2006, making it the first country to independently design and develop such a project.[26] The temperature milestone is only the first step, as China will next need to figure out how to maintain the reaction for more than a few seconds and make the technology commercially viable.[27]

China is also looking at thorium-based molten salt reactors, which have an advantage of being self-regulating and failsafe, on top of being harder to weaponize. Research for thorium reactors began in the 1970s at the Oak Ridge National Laboratory in the US, but China is picking up the torch with the expectation of possible operations and grid integrations within fifteen years.[28]

China's investments in the nuclear technologies of today and tomorrow will play a big role in the country's nuclear global ambitions. The Asian powerhouse could play a critical role in reducing carbon emissions domestically and internationally while also increasing the country's geopolitical leverage as it finances and develops nuclear reactors abroad in the future.

STORAGE

As China ramps up intermittent wind and solar resources, the country is investing in adding energy storage to the grid, particularly lithium-ion and flow batteries. Chinese regulators approved a $174 million investment in a lithium-ion project that would store energy for up to four hours, and they commented that future expansion of this project will depend on market conditions and the needs of the grid.[29] Lithium-ion is the same storage technology found in electric vehicles and the cell phone.

China is also approving and deploying flow batteries, which use resources that are more strategic to China. VRB Energy, a major developer of flow batteries, is deploying several projects in China. Jim Stover, the VP of Business Development at VRB, commented that: "The Chinese government, I think in particular, is happy to incentivize or call out vanadium like this. They want to push a number of technologies, but there is an awful lot of vanadium resources in China, both from mine sites and from steel slag recovery. They're trying to seize that as a good and natural fit, they don't have a lot of lithium. They have a lot of lithium manufacturers but not a lot of lithium itself, or cobalt, or nickel even."[30]

As China ramps up solar and wind in the new few decades, energy storage will play a bigger and bigger role on the grid to balance the supply and demand. Storage will also be a major need for international countries as they transition their grids to clean energy, so China is looking to be a major innovator in this space. China is already the top innovator for lithium-ion batteries, as major headway in electronics and electric vehicles has allowed innovation to thrive. We will discuss this in the next chapter about transportation.

INTERNATIONAL POWERHOUSE AND WORLD LEADER

China strongly supports industries that will help the country become self-sufficient, such as the significant investments and initiatives behind renewable and clean energy. After significant investments in China's domestic market, Chinese corporations have now become manufacturing powerhouses around the world. Furthermore, China is literally buying influence throughout the world, especially with developing countries, by financing and building infrastructure projects, such as energy projects. China's push for clean energy is leading the country to become the leading powerhouse and the leading geopolitical driver in the Clean Revolution around the globe.

THE FUTURE OF CLEAN ENERGY

"Wind and solar are set to surge to almost "50 by 50" – 50% of world generation by 2050 – on the back of precipitous

reductions in cost, and the advent of cheaper and cheaper batteries that will enable electricity to be stored and discharged to meet shifts in demand and supply. Coal shrinks to just 11% of global electricity generation by 2050."

—BLOOMBERG NEW ENERGY FINANCE'S

(BNEF) NEW ENERGY OUTLOOK 2018

I will be the first to admit I'm not a forecaster, but I will say I'm very bullish on the future prospects of clean energy as solar, wind, and batteries continuously drop in price. Just like we could have predicted the future of computers through Moore's Law decades ago by looking at trend lines, we can also look to the future of clean energy with data. The best source of forecasting for the future of clean energy has been Bloomberg New Energy Finance (BNEF), which is a group of energy experts around the world that use the "world's most sophisticated data sets to create clear perspectives and in-depth forecasts that frame the financial, economic and policy implications of industry-transforming trends and technologies."[31]

The top highlights from BNEF's New Energy Outlook 2018 report include:

- *50 by 50: Cheap renewable energy and batteries fundamentally reshape the electricity system. Batteries boom means that half of the world's electricity by 2050 will be generated from wind and solar.*

- **PV, wind, and batteries trifecta**: *The cost of an average PV plant falls 71% by 2050. Wind energy is getting cheaper too, and we expect it to drop 58% by 2050. PV and wind are already cheaper than building new large-scale coal and gas plants. Batteries are also dropping dramatically in cost. Cheap batteries enable wind and solar to run when the wind isn't blowing and the sun isn't shining.*

- **Coal is the biggest loser in this outlook**: *Coal will shrink to just 11% of global electricity generation by 2050, from 38% currently.*

- **Gas consumption for power generation increases only modestly out to 2050**: *despite growing capacity, as more and more gas-fired facilities are either dedicated peakers or run at lower capacity factors helping to balance variable renewables, rather than run flat-out around-the-clock. Gas use declines dramatically in Europe, grows in China and picks up materially in India beyond 2040.*

- **Electric vehicles add around 3,461TWh of new electricity demand globally by 2050, equal to 9% of total demand**: *Time-of-use tariffs and dynamic charging further support renewables integration: they allow vehicle owners to choose to charge during high-supply, low-cost periods, and so help to shift demand to periods when cheap renewables are running.*[32]

If BNEF's predictions are correct, transitioning to a 50 percent renewable energy is a massive opportunity for the countries and industries that embrace the Clean Revolution. Coal is on the way out, and solar and wind are the new kids of the block.

* * *

Whereas some of the American political leadership sees the Clean Revolution as a threat to jobs, China sees clean energy as an economic opportunity. Significant investments in solar have led China to be a solar powerhouse, accounting for 60 percent of global supply of solar panels. China is also making significant strides in wind energy, as Chinese companies account for three of the top ten solar manufacturers. In the next chapter, we will discuss how China is innovating in next-generation electric vehicles, which will ultimately be powered by clean energy.

KEY TAKEAWAYS

- **Solar**: China enforced significant mandates and subsidies to support its domestic solar industry. China first pushed solar domestically, but eventually saw a market need in Germany. Now China is the global leader, accounting for 60 percent of solar panel supply. The solar industry was one of the first industries impacted by the US-China trade war under President Trump.

- **Wind**: China made an initial push for wind energy with its "Ride The Wind Programme" in 1997. Wind energy made significant progress through government support: aggressive wind energy targets, pre-determined wind-rich zones, feed-in tariffs, priority access to the grid, interconnection coordination, competitive bidding, and localization (70 percent local production). Chinese wind manufacturers now account for three of the top ten global companies.

- **Hydro**: China is building a lot of new hydropower plants, accounting for 40 percent of the global hydro construction. Chinese companies are also building hydropower projects around the world, including in the Americas.

- **Nuclear**: While the world is moving away from nuclear energy, China is going headfirst into advancing this sector. Even US-based nuclear companies are looking to China as an innovation test bed. China is also investing in other nuclear technologies, like nuclear fusion and thorium-based reactors.

- **Storage**: China's push into electric vehicles is helping to develop its domestic battery industry, which will play a significant role in balancing energy when the sun isn't shining and the wind isn't blowing. Storage will play a big role in both energy and transportation.

- **The Future**: BNEF estimates the electricity market will be 50 percent renewables by 2050. That puts China in a strategic advantage, as Chinese companies already dominate the solar and wind market.

CHAPTER 5

CHINA'S DISRUPTION
IN CLEAN MOBILITY

———

Major brands are investing and getting behind China's push into clean technologies. China has made significant progress in next-generation transportation, where the country saw a 53 percent increase from the previous year in hybrids and electric vehicles. Decisions in China are affecting major business decisions by American automakers as well. At the end of 2017, General Motors announced it would be launching twenty new electric vehicles over the next five years, with CEO Mary Barra stating that "Clearly we believe the Chinese market will have the highest [number of] electric vehicles most quickly because of the regulatory environment."[1]

This major move by GM was in response to China's announcement to eventually ban the sale of new gas-powered vehicles with no deadline set yet, but China has warned the global market of the direction that the world's biggest auto market is moving. In 2017, China accounted for 35 percent of the global market, whereas the US accounted for only 8.6 percent of the global market. You can see now why even US automakers are looking for hints from China on where the country is going in terms of wants and needs of both the Chinese consumer and the Chinese government.

China already has plans to enter the US market as well. In late 2018, Chinese automaker Qiantu announced that it was looking to enter the US market in 2020. This will be the first time an Asian auto manufacturer enters the US market since Japan's Toyota in the 1970s and Korea's Hyundai in the 1980s. Qiantu would make a luxury car to directly compete with Tesla's luxury models of electric cars.[2] And this could just be the beginning, as the Chinese auto industry becomes more mature and more advanced.

CLEAN MOBILITY

China's major push into electric vehicles creates numerous benefits for the country: become a world leader in the next generation of automotive innovation, reduce the country's dependence on foreign oil, and clean up the country's air pollution problem. America should see this as an opportunity to support our domestic automakers in the transition to electric so they can remain competitive in the global market as the world transitions away from fossil fuels.

China isn't the only country looking to the future, as numerous other major European cities and countries have set deadlines in terms of banning the sale of new gas-powered vehicles, such as the UK, France, Norway, the Netherlands, and more.[3] Most automakers have made some commitment into electric vehicle development, but the real question is who will be the most ambitious and who will get there the fastest to address the world's biggest auto market. Considering that car designs can take years and that retooling the factories will take time as well, the early adopters will have a major head-start on competition, such as Tesla in our own backyard.

CHINA'S SUPPORT

China isn't well known for its cars, as the sector is still young. In 1985, China only produced a total of 5,200 passenger cars, which eventually influenced China to partner with Western firms to develop its own auto industry through joint ventures (JVs). The trend began with Beijing Jeep, a JV with American Motor Company in 1984.

The JV model was finalized through a comprehensive industrial guideline in 1994, requiring majority control to the Chinese party in order to maintain hold on operational decisions. The Chinese party contributed mostly land, workers, and partial capital while the foreign entity contributed to design, manufacturing, marketing, and supply chain logistics. China kept high tariffs on foreign auto imports and kept low tariffs on car parts, while the country worked to advance domestic production of cars and parts.

By 2000, fifteen JVs were in place between Chinese firms and foreign firms from the US, Europe, and Asia. China was successful in reducing imports from 90 percent to 10 percent. However, most of the best-selling domestic models were from the foreign joint brands, and independent Chinese automakers have struggled to gain significant market share. Several independent companies have made progress, such as Geely, BYD, Great Wall, and Chery, which are a mix of private and state-owned enterprises.

As previously mentioned, China's ambitions for EVs stem from becoming more energy independent (as the world's largest oil importer) and address emissions from the transportation sector. From a car manufacturer's perspective, EVs are also less complex than internal combustion engines (ICE), as EVs have fewer parts and batteries are easier to master than an engine, meaning a probable lower barrier to entry into the auto market.

China's push for "new-energy vehicles" (NEVs) has really become a national priority since President Xi has introduced the Made in China 2025. NEVs were one of the top ten priority sectors for the plan, and the goals were to increase the NEV market share for domestic producers to 70 percent by 2020 and 80 percent by 2025, with 80 percent of electric car batteries and engines by 2020.

In 2017, China released its "Medium- and Long-Term Development Plan for the Automotive Industry" with a central target for NEV production to reach two million vehicles by 2020 and account for 20 percent of total auto sales by 2025. China is also looking at three priorities for domestic manufacturers: (1) increase the quality of cars and parts by domestic manufacturers, (2) increase and sustain demand by consumers, governments, and companies for NEVs, and (3) ensure effective charging infrastructure for the increased demand.

SUPPLY

China has advanced NEVs by investing in fundamental R&D, particularly for the battery, engine, and chassis. The battery accounts for 50 percent of a car's production cost, so this area has been a key focus, looking at the entire supply chain from raw materials to manufacturing and recycling. China promoted growth of domestic battery technology by putting forth a "white list" of approved batteries eligible for subsidies, but left out foreign companies like LG and Samsung, despite them having domestic battery facilities. In 2018, they were eventually added to the list, but it's unclear whether the foreign companies will receive subsidies for their batteries.

Over time, foreign auto companies have continued to have a key disadvantage in China. First, as mentioned, the joint ventures required the foreign entities to have minority control. Second, the JVs required some type of technology transfer as a part of the agreement. Finally, in 2017, China has required that new brands are not associated with the foreign partner. Regulatory mandates have put foreign brands at a strategic disadvantage, but in 2018, China has been easing back as China it began eliminating the JV requirements. The first example we have seen is with Tesla, who is now building a factory in China without requiring a joint partner.

China is also pushing NEV technology by implementing a "dual-credit system," where companies are required to hit a minimum proportion and in exchange receive credits for NEV production:

- 4 credits = pure-electric cars (>155 mile range)
- 2 credits = hybrids
- 0 credits = internal combustion engines

Therefore, companies will need to buy credits if they don't hit the threshold or can sell credits if they have a high proposition of NEVs. China first announced the system in 2017, and compliance is set to begin in 2020 with a 10 percent rate for NEVs, rising 2 percent per year.

China has also been pushing NEVs on the consumer side through policies like subsidies, tax benefits, or incentives for consumers or companies. Battery subsidies initially began with consumers in 2010, but eventually they were transitioned to companies to pass savings on to the consumers in 2013. National subsidies were based on the battery range and other performance criteria, with the criteria increasing over time as technology improved. Provinces also provided subsidies, but were capped at 50 percent of the national subsidies.

DEMAND

China has become a major focus for automakers around the globe. From 2002 to 2016 in China, the annual sales of cars, trucks, and buses grew at double-digit annual growth rates, from 2 million units to 28 million units, compared to the global growth rate of 3 percent.[4]

The significant growth can be explained by policies around tax sales cuts or exemptions. Initially to promote all passenger cars, China cut the original 10 percent sales tax to

5 percent in late 2015, raised it to 7.5 percent in 2017, and returned it to 10 percent in 2018. For NEVs, however, sales tax was completely exempt starting in 2014, with a renewed waiver at the end of 2017, extending this exemption until the end of 2020.

NEVs were also incentivized by restricting license issuance for ICE vehicles, making it easier for NEV consumers. The pilot began in 2011, and the policy is now in nineteen cities, which account for 95 percent of sold NEVs in China. For certain cities like Beijing that are looking to control the growth of cars, it's extremely difficult to obtain a license issuance, with a chance of 0.2 percent. Finally, the national government required government agencies, both national and local, to procure NEVs as at least 30 percent of new vehicles starting in 2014, and these government procurement requirements will increase over time.

Electric buses are also a key strategy to air pollution and energy independence. For every one thousand electric buses China puts on the road, the country avoids five hundred barrels of oil consumption per day. Shenzhen became the first major city to implement an all-electric bus fleet in 2017 with a total of sixteen thousand "e-buses," with planning that began in 2013. Nearly 80 percent of the electric buses were made by Shenzhen-based automaker BYD. Furthermore, by the end of 2018, the entire thirteen-thousand-taxi fleet in the city is expected to be 100 percent electric.[5]

Adequate charging infrastructure has a major influence on NEV demand as well, which is why China's various agencies have implemented new initiatives, such as supporting R&D for charging technology and large-scale storage and developing a universal standard for all charging infrastructure.

There are also mandates that charging infrastructure be included in new residential communities, on highways, and in cities. By the first half of 2018, 275,000 charging poles were installed in public areas—a 52 percent increase from the prior year. By 2020, China plans to have a whopping total of 4.5 million poles and 12,000 charging stations.

THE FUTURE

"Our latest forecast shows sales of electric vehicles (EVs) increasing from a record 1.1 million worldwide in 2017, to 11 million in 2025 and then surging to 30 million in 2030 as they become cheaper to make than internal combustion engine (ICE) cars. China will lead this transition, with sales there accounting for almost 50% of the global EV market in 2025."

—BLOOMBERG NEW ENERGY FINANCE'S

(BNEF) ELECTRIC VEHICLE OUTLOOK 2018 REPORT

EVs are already becoming a major market in China, and the Asian powerhouse is on track to be at the forefront of this innovation. In the last chapter, we discussed BNEF's New Energy Outlook, so let's review their five major highlights in their latest Electric Vehicle Outlook 2018:

"By 2040, 55% of all new car sales and 33% of the global fleet will be electric.

China is and will continue to be the largest EV market in the world through 2040.

EV costs. The upfront cost of EVs will become competitive on an unsubsidized basis starting in 2024. By 2029, almost all segments reach parity as battery prices continue to fall.

E-buses. Buses go electric faster than light duty vehicles.

Displacement of transport fuel. Electrified buses and cars will displace a combined 7.3 million barrels per day of transportation fuel in 2040."[6]

BlackRock, the world's largest asset manager with over $6 trillion under management, is also optimistic about next-generation vehicles. The research arm of the firm called BlackRock Investment Institute, put out their "Future of the vehicle" report in 2017, claiming "China, aiming at growing its EV fleet to combat pollution, could account for up to 40% of the hybrids and battery EVs sold annually by 2030."

BREAKDOWN OF GLOBAL CAR SALES BY ENGINE TYPE, 2010–2030

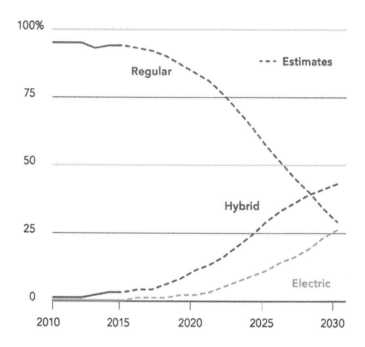

Source: *BlackRock Investment Institute and LMC Automotive, April 2017.*[7]

Over the next decade, we will expect the need for internal combustion engines to decline as hybrid and electric technologies become more prominent in the global transportation system. As the innovative technologies get cheaper and more advanced, NEVs will take significant market share for new car sales globally. Economies of scale will continue the downward trend of battery prices. China will significantly drive down the price of solar, and we could see that same trend for electric vehicles over the next decade.

* * *

As the world moves to reduce carbon emissions, NEVs will become an important part of the strategy for the transportation sector. China is working to address its local air pollution issues and grow its domestic automotive market by pushing significant mandates and subsidies for the next generation of cars, especially for electric and hybrid models. By improving fuel efficiency and transitioning to electric, China is moving its energy economy toward self-sufficiency.

KEY TAKEAWAYS

- **Chinese EV Market**: Automakers around the world are moving their own business strategies as China, the world's biggest car market, announces an eventual ban of internal combustion engine (ICE) vehicles, though no specific deadline has been set yet. China has been pushing their own domestic new-energy vehicle (NEV) market, which will set the Asian powerhouse up for success as numerous countries around the world have already and will continue to ban ICE vehicles at a future date.

- **Supply**: China has supported the advancement of NEVs through various policies, including R&D funding for battery technology, fuel efficiency guidelines, a dual-credit system, and joint venture (JV) mandates.

- **Demand**: China has also supported the adoption of NEVs by consumers through implementing tax incentives/exemptions, license plate restrictions, government procurement requirements, and charging infrastructure funding and mandates.

- **The Future**: Bloomberg New Energy Finance (BNEF) is predicting that 55 percent of all new car sales will be electric by 2040, which will set Chinese automakers up for success in this growing market and inevitable technology.

PART 2

AMERICA'S REBOUND

In the first half, we discussed how the world is pushing forward on climate action and how China is leading the way in cleantech.

In the second half, we will discuss how America can regain our innovative leadership by bold policies to push American scientists, investors, businesses, and jobs.

CHAPTER 6

AMERICA'S ECOSHOT

———

"Innovation distinguishes between a leader and a follower."

—STEVE JOBS, FOUNDER OF APPLE

China currently has the lead in the modern-day Space Race for cleantech, but with American innovation, we still have the ability to catch up and lead this next Industrial Revolution. We need to go back to our innovative roots, as we did in the past. Whenever I think about America's achievements, I first look to national missions, such as being the first to put a man on the moon, the first to open up the internet, or the first to sequence the human genome. American's brand = innovation.

Even our founding fathers were entrepreneurial, setting out to a new land with new opportunities. It's time for America to unleash cleantech innovation in order to compete and win the cleantech race against China. The nation must once again adopt a start-up mindset with our political leaders having a start-up CEO mindset.

AMERICA AS A STARTUP

Any successful start-up has a CEO with a vision. Apple had Steve Jobs, Microsoft had Bill Gates, and Tesla/SpaceX has Elon Musk.

A successful CEO is predominantly focused on asking three questions: (1) Do we have the right <u>vision</u> for the company? (2) Do we the best <u>people</u> in place to achieve that vision? (3) Do we have sufficient <u>money</u> in place to innovate?

Our political leaders should ask the same: (1) Do we have the right vision for our country? (2) Do we the best people in place to achieve that vision? (3) Do we have sufficient funding in place to create an innovative environment for our private sector?

Congress is ultimately the CEO of the United States (not the president). Congress decides where money flows, via the appropriations process. For example, Congress votes whether the Department of Energy (DOE) gets their funding increased, decreased, or status quo. Congress also determines the key people in government. The president appoints key governmental leaders, but Congress (specifically the Senate) is ultimately in charge of confirming political appointees. Congress also decides the laws of the land, so it truly drives the direction and vision of the country.

The real question is: "Where is the vision for America?" Sure, Republican and Democrats have their own party platforms, but it's a wish list, not a focused and bipartisan vision to move our nation forward.

America is known for winning World War II using technology, for being the first to the moon using technology, for creating the world wide web using technology, and leading the effort to sequence the human genome using technology. Seems to be a recurring theme here. Now we need to unleash American innovation for the Clean Revolution and become a world leader in clean technologies.

In order for America to stay globally competitive, we must return to Washington being the "shining city on the Hill," through innovation and technology. We have made major technological achievements by having a vision and putting the proper funding and people behind it.

Let's take a look at some of our past achievements.

THE MANHATTAN PROJECT

When the Allies were losing in World War II, it was time to take drastic measures to put a stop to the deadly global war. The United States, with support from the United Kingdom and Canada, created a project to create the weapon of all weapons: the nuclear bomb. As you know, the nuclear bombs dropped in Nagasaki and Hiroshima led to the end of the war. America accomplished this in a few short years by employing 130,000 people with only a budget of $22 billion (adjusted for inflation). When you put the smartest people in a room with a deadline for action, you make progress.

A major benefit of the Manhattan Project was the nuclear energy programs that began in the US and spread around the world. For decades, nuclear energy was and still is an important energy source for developed countries, and not to mention it was the one of the first large-scale emissions-free energy source we relied on.

THE MOONSHOT GOAL

"We choose to go to the moon. We choose to go to the moon in this decade and do the other things, not because they are easy, but because they are hard, because that goal will serve to organize and measure the best of our energies and skills, because that challenge is one that we are willing to accept, one we are unwilling to postpone, and one which we intend to win, and the others, too." The vision for our mission to the moon was famously given by President John F. Kennedy at Rice University. The Apollo program lasted from 1960 until 1972, and it was estimated that the total program cost approximately $110 billion, adjusted for inflation.[1]

Not only did the US show its power against Russia in the Space Race, but it has also led to the rocket and satellite industries. Semiconductor technology greatly benefited from the Space Race, with US sales of $189 billion, employment of over 250,000 US jobs, and 46 percent domestic share of the global marketplace.[2]

THE HUMAN GENOME PROJECT

The most recent accomplishment by the United States was the sequencing of the human genome. The Human Genome Project (HGP) was administered through the National Institutes of Health (NIH) but carried out by universities and research centers in the US, the UK, Japan, China, Germany, France, and Spain, with over two hundred separate principal investigators.[3] The United States spent over $4 billion (inflation adjusted) on genomic research from 1990 when it officially launched until April 2003 when the sequenced genome was declared completed.[4] Funding came from both the NIH and Department of Energy (DOE), which has ties back to the Manhattan Project because the DOE was interested in the impact of genomic changes to the human body due to atomic radiation.

According to a report by the Battelle Memorial Institute, the HGP has led to $796 billion in economic impact by 2011, which is a big win for our economy! The report notes that the genomic revolution has led to progress in "renewable energy development, industrial biotechnology, agricultural biosciences, veterinary sciences, environmental science, forensic science and homeland security, and advanced studies in zoology, ecology, anthropology and other disciplines."[5]

THE PROBLEM: EMISSIONS AND TIME

To understand why we need an EcoShot, we must dive into the underlying problems – addressing carbon emission and doing it rapidly.

Emissions: the ultimate cause of climate change is carbon emissions in the atmosphere. The release of CO_2 (and other emissions) into the atmosphere creates a greenhouse-like effect, which is why CO_2 is known as a greenhouse gas (GHG). The best analogy I've heard comes from Katharine Hayhoe, a climate scientist. She explains GHGs like blankets: as you add more and more of these GHGs to the atmosphere, the blanket gets thicker, trapping more heat in the atmosphere. The more fossil fuels we burn, the thicker we are making the blanket around our planet.

Therefore, the solution is to get rid of emissions, and there are two ways. The first way is to simply implement clean technologies, such as solar and wind, to avoid burning fossil fuels. The second (and currently more expensive) way is to capture the emissions at the source, such as at a coal or natural gas plant. In this book, when I discuss clean energy, I'm focusing on the outcome (no carbon emissions), not on specific technologies (e.g., solar and wind). People may argue we can achieve 100 percent renewable energy with only wind, solar, and batteries in the US, but I'm viewing it from a global market perspective, where the US can innovate and help other countries transition in the Clean Revolution.

Speed: as mentioned in the introduction, the Clean Revolution is inevitable, but the key issue with climate change is the window is getting narrower and narrower to address global emissions. We have a target carbon "budget" the world must achieve to avoid the worst effects of climate change, and the longer we wait to significantly cut emissions, the more drastic measures the global community will need to implement. For example, the latest report by the Intergovernmental Panel on Climate Change (IPCC) states that emissions need to decline by 45% (from 2010 levels) by 2030.[6] That's 11 years away.

We need to accelerate the pace of innovation, and government support is needed to accelerate the timeline. The private sector will be the key player in innovation, but we need the government to put resources behind the innovation and implementation to support our American entrepreneurs and businesses.

For example, President Bush's EV tax credits were put into place to help America become more independent from foreign oil and gas, which helped launch the EV market in the US. After initial policy support, Tesla later received government loans, which were paid back in full with interest to the government. Now Tesla is a thriving business that is creating jobs, reducing emissions, and helping America become energy independent. The government can help other emerging technologies advance to a mature stage by providing the right incentives and support to the private sector.

Because we will require innovation from the private sector, with the proper policies by the public sector, EcoShot will be a true Public-Private Partnership, with the common interest of reducing emissions through clean technologies. But additionally, we will need people like you to advocate and support our domestic cleantech industries, making it a People-Public-Private Partnership!

THE SOLUTION: AN ECOSHOT

Similar to the Apollo Mission, America's EcoShot will require a few key ingredients in the recipe: (1) a goal with a deadline, (2) smart people, and (3) consistent resources. Political leaders will need to put forward the exact details for the modern-day "mission," but I want to lay out my vision here.

VISION: "To create a sustainable future for our economy, our environment, and our children"

The ultimate vision for America's EcoShot is to create a sustainable future. Our economy relies heavily on fossil fuels, yet fossil fuels are a limited resource and tend to fluctuate in price. The cost of clean technologies is trending in the downward direction while fossil fuels can spike up and down, causing uncertainty for our economy. The vision also looks at our environment, as we move away from fossil fuels, we will avoid devastating oil spills and environmental degradation. And finally, the worst of climate change will most greatly impact the younger generation, including our children and our children's children. The actions we take now will lead to a more sustainable world for future generations.

MISSION: "Become a global leader in clean technologies through embracing American innovation."

The mission of America's EcoShot will succeed with American innovation, with the target of creating and implementing technologies that will move our nation toward zero emissions. As we saw with China, the country first supported its domestic markets for solar, wind, and electric vehicles, and now Chinese companies are thriving competitively around the globe. The US needs to provide the right incentives domestically so we can be the leader internationally. A massive economic opportunity is in front of us to transform the global community to a clean economy.

GOAL: "Transition our economy to 100% clean electricity and clean transportation by 2050"

The goal of our EcoShot will be to cut emissions from the energy and mobility sectors. Other sectors, such as agriculture and industrial processes, are responsible for the carbon emissions as well, but this mission should focus on the biggest problems up front with energy and transportation, which account for over half of emissions in the US. Our first steps should be to decarbonize our electricity and transportation sectors, but this goal will expand to other sectors as policies and technologies become clearer over time.

THE FOUR PILLARS OF CLEANTECH POLICY

Innovate, Incentivize, and Implement — the three ways the US will become a global leader in cleantech. The technologies of tomorrow will require entrepreneurs and scientists to innovate today. The technologies of today will require policies to incentivize adoption of these new innovations while also needing policies to influence implementation by cities, states, and businesses.

Over the next several chapters, we will dive into specific policies that can be embraced by Congress to achieve America's EcoShot. The Four Pillars of Cleantech Policy:

- Advance energy innovation with funding toward research and development
- Implement tax reform to incentivize the adoption of clean technologies
- Implement regulatory reform to ease the implementation of clean technologies
- Provide state grants to help states implement job training programs and clean infrastructure around the country

I'm a realist, so I know that both Republicans and Democrats need to come together in order for this EcoShot to work. For that reason, I have included numerous market-based solutions that conservative policy leaders have put forth as solutions for innovation and implementation. Many of these ideas have been put forward by policy thinkers in our nation, and this book acts as a compilation of the biggest policy ideas that can push our nation forward in this fight as the heavyweight champion of cleantech.

* * *

For our Moonshot, JFK believed in America's science and technical ingenuity. He just had to point to the moon and say we would get there. The rocket scientists didn't know how, and US politicians didn't know the specifics, but we put together a plan and accomplished it. As noted by these achievements, when our nation puts together a vision, puts smart people on the job, and ensures sufficient funding behind the mission, we can make great technological strides. It's time for America's next mission — our EcoShot.

KEY TAKEAWAYS

- **American Achievements**: Government involvement in big national missions shouldn't scare people. The biggest innovations and economic opportunities have come from government programs such as the Apollo Program, the Manhattan Project, and the Human Genome Project. The private sectors were either directly involved in these national projects or they greatly benefited from the technological advancements.

- **EcoShot**: We need a national moonshot to regain global leadership in cleantech. To accomplish this initiative, we will need a national vision, the brightest innovators, and adequate funding. We should put forward a bold vision to move our economy to 100% clean energy and clean transportation. Similar to China, we need to support our domestic market, which will eventually lead to international growth.

- **The 3 I's**: For the remainder of the book, I will review policies that will look to innovate, incentivize, and implement clean technologies. This EcoShot will require bipartisan support, so many of the policies have come from conservative policy thinkers who are concerned about climate change, but want market-driven policies. This isn't a book about "blue" or "red" policies. It's about "red, white, and blue" policies.

"The 'clean energy' challenge deserves a commitment akin to the Manhattan Project or the Apollo moon landing."

—MARTIN REES, SCIENTIST AND FORMER
PRESIDENT OF THE ROYAL SOCIETY

CHAPTER 7

AMERICAN SCIENTISTS

———

"By developing innovative and groundbreaking methods for generating clean, renewable energy, we will help ensure a reliable, affordable power supply, and that our environment is preserved for future generations."

— SUSAN COLLINS, REPUBLICAN SENATOR FROM MAINE

Just like what America did for the Sputnik moment, we will innovate our way to solve climate change and become the dominant leader for clean technologies. An EcoShot will require the smartest minds working on this global issue, so we need significant funding behind innovative cleantech research and projects. A follower looks at a problem and says it's not solvable. A leader looks at a problem and puts the smartest people together with a plan. We have innovative solutions today, like solar, wind, and electric vehicles, but we also need to innovate for the technologies of tomorrow as well. Federal money can provide financial support to the first phase in research & development, as well as to the second phase of implementation.

Government funding of innovation is a major opportunity for the American economy. I've spoken to several conservatives who are pro-fracking for natural gas but against using government dollars for research. They are typically surprised to learn that the technology that caused the natural gas boom in America was actually born out of government research and dollars in partnership with the private sector. Numerous technologies behind hydraulic fracturing ("fracking" for short) came from research at the Department of Energy (DOE). The technology was tested in partnership with Mitchell Energy. The founder George Mitchell is an oil businessman who is now considered the Father of Fracking.

He started Texas-based Mitchell Energy in the 1940s, and throughout the 1970s and 1980s, DOE worked on numerous technologies needed for fracking, such as horizontal drilling, microseismic imaging, and multi-fracture horizontal drilling. With the technology in place, Mitchell Energy was able to perform the first horizontal well in the Texas Barnett Shale in 1991. On top of that, in 1980 Congress passed a production tax credit for unconventional gas, which also assisted on the finance side with this new technology.

Dan Steward, the former Vice President for Mitchell Energy, discussed the DOE's role during a 2011 interview:

"In the seventies we started running out of gas, and that's when the DOE started looking for more. The DOE's [Eastern Gas Shales Project] determined there was a hell of a lot of gas in shales. We got the DOE and the GRI [Gas Research Institute] involved in the Barnett in the early 1990s. Mitchell hadn't wanted to get them involved because we were trying to understand it and didn't want competition for the Barnett until we had a handle on what we were doing.

By the early 1990s, we had a good position, acceptable but lacking a knowledge base, and then Mitchell said 'Okay, I'm open to bringing in DOE and GRI' in 1991. Mitchell was selling his gas a dollar and a quarter over the spot price. Mitchell had the money to invest in R&D. So you could say that those pricing scenarios, and the tax credit, created the possibility for shale gas. DOE started it, and other people took the ball and ran with it. You cannot diminish DOE's involvement."[1]

Government research today is making a big impact on American businesses. Our national labs have played a key role, as research out of Argonne National Laboratory is now found in battery technologies in both the Chevrolet Volt and the Ford Focus EV.[2] Government research and funding doesn't replace the innovation in our private sector. It actually advances it.

INNOVATION GRANTS FOR R&D

One of the earliest successes of government-supported research came out of the Department of Defense (DOD), which has an innovation arm called Defense Advanced Research Projects Agency (DARPA). A project was started by J.C.R. Licklider, who was the director of Information Processing Techniques Office (IPTO) at ARPA, which it was called then. He had previously written a paper called "On-Line Man Computer Communication" discussing a connected global network, and he had the vision to connect the three distant locations of the DOD's computers.

Later, Robert Taylor become the new director at IPTO and was successful in creating a network between the three computers on October 29, 1969, called the Arpanet. By 1972, the first communication (AKA email) was sent, and by 1973, people were calling it the "internet"—something you may have heard of.[3] A side project at the DOD led to the biggest innovation of the century.

DARPA was born out of the launch of Sputnik in 1957, leading to its mission "to make pivotal investments in breakthrough technologies for national security." With the Sputnik surprise, America decided "it would be the initiator and not the victim of strategic technological surprises," according to DARPA's website. The agency goes for "transformation change instead of incremental advances."[4]

Similar to the concern around Sputnik, the National Academy of Sciences along with the National Academy of Engineering sensed an eroding of science and technology that could jeopardize America's future prosperity. In 2005, there was not only a trend of manufacturing moving overseas, but also jobs in other areas, such as finance, engineering, and research. Senator Lamar Alexander (R-Tennessee) noted the concern and asked for organizations to pull together experts and stakeholders to provide recommendations to Congress. The final deliverable was a 2006 report called "Rising Above the Gathering Storm: Energizing and Employing America for a Brighter Future," which ultimately looked at the top ten actions that "federal policymakers could take to enhance the science and technology enterprise so that the United States can successfully compete, prosper, and be secure in the global community of the 21st century." For the section around scientific research, the report recommended "Use DARPA as a model for energy research."[5]

From that 2006 report, ARPA-E was finally born in 2007 through the America COMPETES Act, though no budget was given. The program was finally funded through the economic stimulus package in 2009 and is housed under the DOE. Since then, ARPA-E has shown significant progress, evident by its bipartisan support. In 2018, the Trump administration requested to completely eliminate ARPA-E, but instead the Republican-controlled Congress actually gave a $47 million increase for a total budget of $353 million in the 2018 appropriations bill.[6]

Senator Alexander, the same individual who asked for the report that eventually led to ARPA-E, at the time was Chair of the Energy and Water Development Appropriations Subcommittee. He gave an opening message at the 2018 ARPA-E Innovation Summit, commenting that "one thing we do better than any country in the world is innovation through research." He also noted that ARPA-E doesn't "compete with the private sector. ARPA-E gets the ball rolling for the private sector on technologies that stand to greatly benefit taxpayers." He bragged that 136 ARPA-E-funded projects have attracted $2.6 billion in reported funding from the private sector.[7]

ENERGY MOONSHOTS

Another innovative program that has come out of DOE is The SunShot Initiative, which was launched in 2011. The goal of the project was to cut the cost of solar energy (for residential, commercial, and utility-scale) by 75 percent by the end of the decade—an aggressive target at that time. Cutting utility-scale solar by 75 percent would make it cost competitive with existing polluting plants. On September 12, 2017, DOE announced that the initiative had reached its goal three years early! The initiative continues with a 2030 goal to cut utility-scale solar by 50 percent in order to be much cheaper than existing polluting plants.[8] You can check out the targets for each sector in the next chart.

Jigar Shah, the former CEO of solar company SunEdison and now clean energy financier, said in our discussion that the SunShot program was most beneficial on reducing soft costs for deployment, so he believes "DOE should be focused on the soft costs of these technologies." Soft costs is an engineering term that includes everything outside of direct construction costs, such as architectural, engineering, financing, regulatory, environmental study, and legal fees.

SUNSHOT PROGRESS AND GOALS

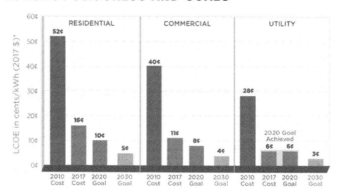

Levelized cost of energy (LCOE) progress and targets are calculated based on average U.S. climate and without the ITC or state/local incentives. The residential and commercial goals have been adjusted for inflation from 2010-17.

Source: Department of Energy's SunShot Initiative[8]

We should take the lessons learned from the SunShot Initiative and apply them to other areas in clean energy and electric transportation. I'm calling for a $10 billion investment in ten moonshot cleantech efforts to support our scientists and innovators around the country.

	INITIATIVE	FOCUS	DESCRIPTION
1	**SunShot**	Solar energy	We should continue the innovation in residential, commercial, and utility-scale solar energy.
2	**WindShot**	Wind Energy	We begin pushing both on-shore and off-shore wind energy. The Midwest is a growing area for on-shore wind energy, while the US is surrounded by water, so we can advance off-shore wind energy as well.
3	**AtomShot**	Advanced nuclear energy	American innovators are already working on advanced nuclear fission technologies, such as molten salt reactors, so we should put more money into supporting these entrepreneurs. We should invest more into fusion technologies.
4	**StorageShot**	Energy storage technologies	As solar and wind become major energy providers on the grid, we will need to figure out how to effectively store energy when the sun doesn't shine and the wind doesn't blow, both short term and long term. Lithium-ion batteries have made significant advancements due to the use in computers and smartphones, but other battery technologies can play a role, like flow batteries.

5	**HydroShot**	Hydropower	Hydropower has been a key provider of electricity for decades in the US, so we need to put a mix of funding toward advancing turbines while also putting money toward implementing turbines into non-powered dams. Run-of-the-river innovation can also reduce ecological impact of dams. Other water-based technologies, such as marine and hydrokinetic, should be explored.
6	**GeoShot**	Geothermal energy	Geothermal has potential in several regions around the country. The resource is also considered renewable, as the heat from the Earth is constant.
7	**CarbonShot**	Carbon capture technologies	As the globe transitions their energy systems, coal and natural gas will likely remain prevalent over the next few decades, so we need technologies to (1) capture carbon at power plants, as well as (2) take carbon directly out of the air.
8	**FuelShot**	Alternative fuels	I believe our passenger car sector will move toward hybrid and electric vehicles, but we still need to think about other sectors as well, like the aviation and shipping sectors, so we will still need advancements in alternative fuels.
9	**EfficiencyShot**	Energy efficient appliances	Many devices in our homes and businesses require energy, such as heating, air conditioning, lighting, and more. We should continue to push for energy-efficient appliances to cut our need for energy. Furthermore, opportunities exist to address carbon emissions associated with industrial processes, such as aluminum smelting.
10	**GridShot**	Grid technologies	As solar, wind, storage, and other technologies feed energy to our energy system, we will need to modernize our grid. Also, electric transportation will add demand to the grid, so we need effective technologies to ensure a reliable grid.

IMPLEMENTATION LOANS

Not only do we need to push innovation of technologies but we also need to push implementation of technologies. Experience curves are the key reason we've seen significant drops in the cost of solar, wind, and battery technology. The experience curve was termed by Bruce Henderson in the 1960s, explaining that the cost per unit of a product comes down as the cumulative volume of production goes up.[9] It applies to most industrial sectors, but the origin came from the aircraft industry. The Air Force scientists noticed that the cost of each additional plane declined and production increased. The same can be applied to clothing, auto, computer, pharmaceutical, and of course the energy industry. Many of the efficiencies came from product re-designs, labor efficiency, economies of scale, and process improvement.[10]

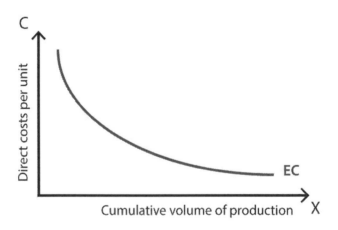

The concept can be applied to fracking. Lots of technologies and research went into this innovative methodology, but the cost of fracking dropped as companies built new practices on top of this underlying technology. Moore's law is indirectly tied to this concept. The computing power doubles every eighteen months, or in other words, the cost of the same computing power is halved every eighteen months. We see that in clean energy as well. Swanson's law states that "with every doubling of production and shipments of panels, there has been a 20 percent reduction in the cost of panels." The law was named after Richard Swanson, the founder of solar company SunPower.

SWANSON'S LAW

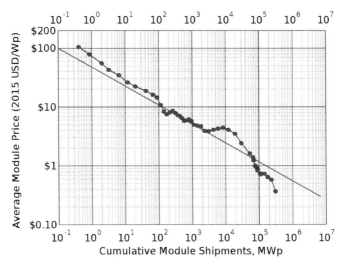

As you can see above, as the cumulative panels are produced, the average panel cost is coming down significantly. Due to the high upfront costs of innovation, many companies are more comfortable making minor improvements to their current technologies. With any investment, there is a balance of risk and reward. From a business standpoint, some breakthrough technologies might be too high risk and require a high amount of investment due to the amount of time it will take to bring the cost down. This is a perfect opportunity for our federal programs to help with more of the risky research upfront.

Government officials need to understand that not every research investment is going to work out. I think both sides of the aisle understand this with medical research. The NIH gets over $37 billion in funding per year, with 80 percent of the funding going toward outside research at universities, medical schools, and research institutions, with 10 percent of the budget for internal research at the NIH.[11]

The reason America is the top in the world for pharmaceutical R&D is because we invest a lot of federal dollars into new, risky opportunities. Of the $37 billion NIH receives to help with medical breakthroughs, only 1 in 5,000–10,000 drug candidates make it from "bench side to bedside."[12] We know a majority of research projects aren't going to find positive results, but several breakthroughs make up for all the failures. Research dollars need to be looked at it from a lens similar to what venture capitalists (VCs) see for start-up investing. The one-in-ten rule of thumb means that 90 percent of your investments will fail, but the 10 percent winners that succeed will make up for the losses.

When companies are looking to get new technology off the ground, it's difficult to get the necessary capital from traditional sources, as banks are risk averse. That's where DOE's Loan Program Office (LPO) comes into play to assist innovators. The program was created in 2005 under President Bush, with funding added under President Obama. To commercialize innovation, projects eventually reach the *Valley of Death*, where there are insufficient funds for large-scale projects, such as building utility-scale solar projects or retooling expansive auto manufacturing plants.

THE VALLEY OF DEATH

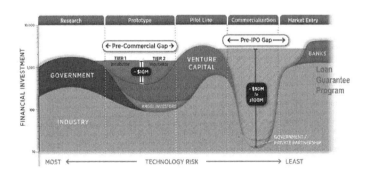

Source: Solar Energy Industries Association – Loan Guarantee Program[13]

A spokesperson from the DOE stated in a Greentech Media article: "The goal of the Department's loan guarantee program is to fund innovative, clean energy technologies at scale that would otherwise have a difficult time finding funding in the private markets while also creating jobs in communities around the country. To date, the loan program has committed to or finalized more than $30 billion in loan guarantees for twenty-nine clean energy projects, which have created or saved over 62,000 jobs. The program does not distinguish between technologies, instead focusing on an 'all-of-the-above' approach that has resulted in investments in an array of energy sectors including solar, wind, geothermal, transmission, energy storage, energy efficiency, biofuels, nuclear, and advanced technology vehicles."[14]

Tesla is the golden child for the Program. In 2010 in the middle of the recession, DOE issued a $465 million loan (with matching private funds) to Tesla through its Advanced Technology Vehicles Manufacturing (ATVM) Program, with $100 million going toward the manufacturing plant and $365 million toward the production engineering and assembly of the plug-in electric vehicles.[15]

A few short years later in 2013, Tesla announced it had paid back the entire loan with interest nine years early.[16] Today, the Fremont facility itself employs 10,000 people, and Tesla globally employed about 37,500 workers by the end of 2017.[17] Furthermore, loans have also been provided for next-generation solar projects, like the $90 million loan guarantee for Colorado's Alamosa Solar Generating Plant, which is the first utility-scale high concentration photovoltaic (HCPV) solar generation project in the US and also the largest HCPV project in the world.[18]

The LPO currently has $40 billion in loans and loan guarantees available for large-scale energy infrastructure for these key areas:

- Innovative Energy Loan Guarantee Program
  - Advanced Fossil Energy ($8.5 billion)
  - Advanced Nuclear Energy ($12.5 billion)
  - Renewable Energy & Efficient Energy ($4.5 billion)
- Advanced Technology Vehicles Manufacturing Program ($16 billion)
- Tribal Energy Loan Guarantee Program ($2 billion)

As innovation in cleantech grows, we will need to expand these loans to help our inventors and entrepreneurs commercialize technologies to ensure American innovation is making it to the market.

* * *

For energy innovation, research dollars and loan guarantees need to go hand in hand. The moonshot goals for clean energy and transportation require research dollars to the smartest minds around the country in our national labs, universities, and small businesses. The Loan Guarantee Program is basically phase two of the moonshot goals. Let's make sure these innovative technologies can be deployed and eventually commercialized into new American businesses.

KEY TAKEAWAYS

- **Innovation Grants**: The Department of Energy's (DOE) Advanced Research Projects Agency-Energy (ARPA-E), which was modeled after Department of Defense's (DOD) DARPA program, would be a perfect avenue for rapidly expanding R&D efforts in the United States, helping our country compete with China.

- **Energy Moonshots**: The US had great success as a part of its SunShot Initiative, which had a goal to bring down the cost of residential and utility-scale solar energy. We should expand this program to look at ten areas of innovation, putting $1 billion in each area of innovation, including, but not limited to, technologies in: solar, wind, geothermal, hydropower, energy storage, carbon capture, next-generation nuclear, next-generation fuels (hydrogen fuel cells and biofuels), efficient appliances, and grid technologies. Right now, the current budget of ARPA-E is around $300 million, but we should significantly expand this funding to $10 billion to help America become the leader in cleantech innovation.

- **Implementation Loans**: As we see feasible technologies come out of our research, we need to provide financial opportunities for our businesses when they reach the *Valley of Death*. Through the DOE's Loan Program Office, we can provide loans to businesses that need to deploy new innovations on a large scale. Energy innovation is an infrastructure, which requires significant capital to move beyond the research and development stage.

"If there is a 90% chance of failure on a transformative project, then we have a 10% chance of transforming the world. That's pretty great."

—VINOD KHOSLA, FOUNDER OF CLEANTECH
VENTURE CAPITAL FIRM KHOSLA VENTURES

CHAPTER 8

AMERICAN INVESTORS

___

"If you want more of something, subsidize it; if you want less of something, tax it."

—RONALD REAGAN, US PRESIDENT

In order to transition America to a clean economy, we are going to need an abundance of investors looking to invest in the Clean Revolution. Investors range from American citizens to business owners and corporations. Tax policy can be an avenue to influence the influx of billions of dollars into cleantech solutions in both energy and transportation.

Tax reform will advance innovation and implementation in cleantech, while also being a great way to bring both political parties to the table. I think there is a strong bipartisan approach here to make our cleantech industries more globally competitive against China, while also improving our own environment in our communities.

CLEAN TAX CUTS

Clean Tax Cuts (CTCs) are an innovative policy concept put forth by the Grace Richardson Fund, a nonprofit that "pioneers new free market policy solutions to critical issues stuck in partisan gridlock."[1] Rod Richardson came up with the idea for CTCs in 2001 to advance clean energy investments, but he didn't publicly pursue the idea until 2016.[2]

Since then, Richardson has put together expert working groups to collaborate and discuss how tax incentivizes can influence people, businesses, and financiers to invest in cleaner solutions. He believes if you want more of something, tax it less. This could be evident by the popularity of real estate investing, where significant investors can take advantage of tax incentives.

With CTCs, tax incentives can help significant capital flow into these cleaner technologies. CTCs are focused around tying incentives to metrics or outcomes (e.g., reducing carbon emissions), rather than tying it to specific technologies (e.g., solar vs. nuclear). What the climate movement really needs is money coming out of dirty investments, like polluting power plants, and toward clean investments, like solar and wind projects. Tax incentives can help influence the flow of money from one stream to another.

Incentivizing the private sector to invest in clean projects could create significant changes. Just look at Apple, who issued a $1.5 billion "green bond" in 2016, the largest bond ever issued for a corporation. The bond goes toward clean energy and green building projects in Apple's global supply chain, and Apple expects a majority of the proceeds will go into effect within two years.[3] According to Apple's bond audits, the projects involve: renewable energy, pollution prevention and control, sustainable water management, eco-efficient technologies, and energy efficiency.[4] Bonds are just one way corporations can help move this momentum forward. Let's check out some interesting tax-specific concepts in various sectors.

ENERGY

Oil and gas companies have been around for decades and have had a track record of easily obtaining funding for their capital needs. The issue with newer and more innovative clean energy, like solar and wind, is that there is a shorter track record, meaning companies struggle to find adequate funding with competitive terms. Research suggests that to limit global warming to the 2°C target, we would need to see global investments in wind and solar around $500 billion per year over the next twenty-five years. However, in 2016, global investments in solar and wind were only $226 billion, so we need double the capital flow into the clean energy markets.[5]

"Green Bonds" have already been tested out through the municipal market, allowing investors to invest in their community while getting tax-free returns. The interest paid on municipal bonds (or "muni bonds") are exempt from federal taxes, so many investors see muni bonds as an attractive investment. Muni bonds are a $3.7 trillion market, while higher-yielding taxable corporate bonds are a $35 trillion market—ten times larger! We could have a swarm of new investors getting into *tax-free corporate green bonds* by exempting the interest income from federal taxes as well. Here are two policy ideas put forward on how to implement this:

Emission Reduction Bonds (ERBs): "ERBs would eliminate federal taxes on interest income from bonds or loans invested in projects that meet the test of being an emissions-free energy generator, thus rewarding investments in clean energy infrastructure like wind, solar, nuclear and geothermal projects. Approved and verified technologies installed and put into service would qualify for the 100 percent tax cut exemption on all loan or bond debt interest." This could have a big impact by allowing corporations to put out tax-free bonds, which would attract investors into providing capital to these clean energy projects.

Clean Asset Bonds (CABs): CABs are similar to ERBs, but extend to infrastructure and projects that relate to the implementation of clean energy, "where the underlying assets deliver or support a known, quantifiable benefit, or are impact-certified by an external standard such as ENERGY STAR or CAFE. These qualify as "clean" without further external assessment by virtue of proven ability to reduce waste, inefficiency, and negative externalities." CABs could be used to finance projects such as:

- *"Renewable and other low or zero emission energy infrastructure projects (ERBs)*
- *Electric or [plug-in electric hybrid] PEH private vehicles, service fleets, and public transportation*
- *Energy storage, batteries, and fuel cells; smart grids and transmission*
- *Green buildings and energy efficiency equipment (e.g., ENERGY STAR loans and MBS [mortgage-backed security])*
- *Oil & Gas, industrial, community waste reduction, monitoring and recycling systems*
- *CCUS [Carbon Capture, Utilization, and Storage], Air Capture, and downstream captured carbon product manufacture*
- *Factories, manufacture, construction and installation for all the above"[5]*

People could argue that corporate bonds shouldn't be tax exempt, but similar to muni bonds, these green bonds ultimately provide a public benefit for all by transitioning away from polluting sources of energy and implementing cleaner solutions.

Zero Emissions Energy Tax Credit: To understand this policy concept, you first need to understand how utilities make money. For-profit utilities, also known as investor-owned utilities (IOUs), are guaranteed a rate of return for building energy projects. IOUs typically make an 8–10 percent return on their capital projects[6,] so if a project costs $100 million dollars, the utility will profit $8-10 million. Therefore, IOUs are incentivized to create bigger and more expensive projects to increase their profit. However, the project has to be approved through a "rate case" in front of state regulators, where IOUs make their arguments to build an energy project and the Public Utility Commission (PUC) has to make a decision while also considering alternative options. Ultimately, the tax on this project is passed on to ratepayers—you and me—through our electricity bills.

A policy has been put forth by Paul Walker at ConservAmerica, which is a nonpartisan, nonprofit organization focused on environmental and energy issues, but has been included in Rod Richardson's reports. The so-called "Zero Regrets" Policy "eliminates taxes on the revenues earned from producing energy with a zero emissions approach (nuclear, wind, hydro-power, solar, and geothermal)."[7]

Since tax changes are ultimately passed on to ratepayers, eliminating federal taxes for clean energy revenues could cut utility rates for ratepayers in thirty-three states where IOUs still are in place. For example, if the PUC was considering an equivalent cost project between natural gas versus solar + storage—let's say $10 million for simplicity—the PUC could lean toward choosing the solar project because it would ultimately save ratepayers money by avoiding passing the taxes on to utility bills. This is a win-win-win situation: utilities get lower tax rates for clean energy projects, ratepayers get lower electricity bills, and our communities get cleaner air!

ENERGY EFFICIENCY

In the US, over 5.5 million commercial buildings exist, with 43 percent of buildings being owner occupied, 34 percent leased, and 23 percent government-owned. Approximately 20–35 percent of commercial building floor area is owned by Real Estate Investment Trusts (REITs), limited liability corporations (LLCs) and limited liability partnerships (LLPs). It is estimated that $72 billion worth of energy efficiency projects are available in the US. If we can provide enough incentives for real estate investors to invest in energy efficiency projects, we could really cut down on our energy demand around the country while also creating American jobs.

The Grace Richardson Fund, along with the American Council for an Energy Efficient Economy (ACEEE), put together a working group to look at various options, coming up with two tax policy proposals:

- **Reduced Clean Tax Rate**: Simply, an ENERGY STAR-rated building will receive a lower tax rate, perhaps similar to long-term capital gains rates instead of the usual marginal tax rates. The Environmental Protection Agency (EPA) has an ENERGY STAR rating program, so an "efficiency benchmark" is already in practice that scales from 1 to 100. Buildings that score 75 or above would be eligible for a reduced tax rate, which would last for five years. After the five-year window, owners could get a 30 percent savings relative to their new tax rate. As cities grow and new buildings are built, this tax incentive could really push developers to strongly consider ENERGY STAR-rated buildings.

- **Clean Accelerated Depreciation**: According to the tax code, a commercial building depreciates over thirty-nine years after the build or purchase of the building. The thirty-nine-year period also applies to building enhancements, such as HVAC or lighting upgrades, which can have a shorter lifetime around fifteen years. Tenant improvements, however, can be depreciated over fifteen years. Accelerated depreciation means rather than spreading depreciation out over the full thirty-nine years, investors can gain more benefits upfront by accelerating the timeframe. The working group recommended the following: "Buildings achieving 30 percent energy savings earn immediate expensing; 20 percent energy savings earns five-year depreciation, and 10 percent savings earns ten-year expensing."[8] Therefore, the buildings with the biggest potential for energy efficiency gains will receive a bigger upfront tax incentive.

As more cleantech innovations are created for achieving energy efficiency, these tax incentives could help grow the current efficiency market. Once again, this is a win-win-win situation. Building owners can achieve energy savings, the market for energy efficiency technology could grow, and we could reduce our current reliance on polluting power plants.

TRANSPORTATION

The automotive industry currently has standards that are set by the government to achieve fuel economy. President Nixon put the Corporate Average Fuel Economy (CAFE) standards in place after the 1973 Oil Embargo to decrease our dependency on foreign oil, particularly from Saudi Arabia. President Bush later increased these standards again in 2007 during another period when oil prices rapidly increased.

Because of these CAFE standards, the auto industry already has targets in place. Right now, automakers have only penalties in place if the standards are not reached.

In a unique approach, by reducing tax rates for automakers with fuel-efficient fleets, it could incentivize automakers to invest in cleaner vehicles. The idea put forth by R Street Institute, a conservative think tank, would lower tax rates when the automaker's fleet meets fuel economy metrics, as put forward by the CAFE standards. Ultimately, the lower the fleet emissions, the lower the tax rate for the automaker.

The proposal explains the impact of this policy concept:

"If applied to all capital taxes (corporate income tax as well as taxes paid by investors on capital gains, dividends and interest) that would provide a very powerful mechanism to drive the automobile industry ever-cleaner. Firms with cleaner fleets would decrease taxes, lower cost of capital, and increase returns, gaining significant competitive advantages over less efficient firms. Since every board member, executive, and employee has a stock package, the value of which increases as taxes go down, CTC applied to all capital taxes presents a powerful point of leverage to incent and align corporate behavior and culture, at every level, with the goal of reducing waste and inefficiency."

Using CTCs for automakers could help reduce emissions in the transportation sector while also allowing automakers to have more capital for further innovation.

We also previously mentioned Carbon Asset Bonds (CABs), so CABs could be used to finance auto projects as well, such as "the manufacture of electric and hybrid vehicles, and components thereof, or other kinds of low emission vehicles, the purchase and operation of high-efficiency service fleets, public EV charging infrastructure, as well as mass transportation alternatives."[9] If automakers could get access to more money through tax-free corporate green bonds, you could see automakers investing more in clean vehicle infrastructure.

If we can incentivize automakers through taxes to invest in fuel-efficient vehicles, we could achieve a multi-win situation: automakers have more capital for innovation, consumers have more fuel efficient cars, we get cleaner air, and America can decrease our reliance on foreign oil and gas!

EMERGING ENERGY CREDITS

The Emerging Energy Tax Credits (EETCs) is a technology-neutral incentive for emerging energy technologies, where the incentives ramp down as the production scales up. The policy idea has been put forward by the Clean Capitalists

Coalition, which is a group of experts, businesses, and investors that recommends clean energy policies.

The purpose of EETCs is to facilitate entrepreneurs and businesses to innovate and create new technologies that can provide clean energy to the grid. Two types of EETCs could be implemented for an emerging energy investment credit (EEICs) and an emerging energy production credit (EEPCs). For investments, the coalition has proposed a tax credit of 30 percent, a similar tax credit percentage received by wind and solar today. For production, incentives would ramp down as production scales up. Here's the proposed scaling:

- Tax credit worth 60% for a technology < 0.5% of national electricity generation
- Tax credit worth 40% for a technology < 1% of national generation
- Tax credit worth 30% for a technology < 1.5% of national generation
- Tax credit worth 15% for a technology < 2% of national generation[10]

The phasing out of these tax credits means that emerging technologies can get their footing in the market while they scale up and compete with incumbent technologies in the early stages of innovation. Both the investment and production tax credits could help push entrepreneurs and investors into the market. As solar and wind become more prominent, we are seeing the early stages of utilities testing out energy storage on the grid, so emerging storage technologies can greatly benefit from EETCs. Jigar Shah, who is the former cofounder of solar company SunEdison and cofounder and current President at Generate Capital, believes some of these emerging technologies, such as storage, geothermal, and small hydro, will be part of the mix but "hasn't reach the same level of scale and standardization that drove cost reduction for the solar industry."

In the past, Congress has given specific tax credits to specific technologies, but we can support all emerging technologies by implementing this technology-neutral tax policy. Let's influence our innovators and investors to put money toward our clean transition.

For more information on this policy concept, check out Clean Capitalist Coalition at cleancapitalistcoalition.org.

MASTER LIMITED PARTNERSHIPS

Master Limited Partnerships (MLPs) are an example of how the fossil fuel industry receives special treatment in our tax code, creating an uneven playing field. An MLP is a fancy corporate status, where it has the tax benefits of a partnership (taxed only at the investor level), but it has the liquidity of a publicly traded company. Nearly 82 percent of MLPs were used for "depletable natural resources," with the remainder in real estate and other sectors. We should create an even playing field by allowing clean energy projects to take advantage of MLPs as well—not just oil and gas companies.

Because these units are publicly traded, MLPs allow projects to access cheaper capital. American Wind Energy Association, the trade association for wind energy, noted that expanding MLPs to renewables could lead to an additional "$3.2 billion to $5.6 billion capital inflow into the industry between [2018] and 2021."[11]

Luckily in 2017, a bipartisan bill was introduced in the Senate called the MLP Parity Act, but has yet to be voted on by Congress. MLPs could be used by projects in wind, solar, nuclear, energy efficiency, carbon capture, and other emerging technologies. Let's create a financially level playing field for every energy technology, not just for oil and gas. This would allow any American to invest in and receive money from clean energy projects, including you and me.

ELECTRIC VEHICLE INCENTIVES

You either lived through or have studied in school about the 1973 Oil Crisis. Americans faced major issues when oil prices doubled and then quadrupled, leading to gas shortages across the United States. Lines of cars filled the streets waiting at gas stations with little to no gas. The shortage was so severe that President Nixon requested American citizens consider conservation measures. The crisis led to President Nixon's Project Independence to promote domestic energy independence. The goal was to achieve energy self-sufficiency by 1980 by looking at energy conservation and alternative sources of energy.

The real move to energy security is not to have more fuel-efficient vehicles, but actually to electrify our transportation sectors, of which passenger cars make up a majority on our roads. We can do so by continuing to incentivize electric vehicle adoption around the US as the technology improves. The "political father" of the electric car industry is President Bush, who signed the EV tax credit into law as a part of the Energy Independence and Security Act of 2007.

At the federal level, you can receive a tax credit for up to $7,500 for qualified electric and plug-in hybrid electric vehicles (PHEV), depending on the size of the battery, that were purchased during or after 2010. All-electric vehicles receive the full $7,500 while the rebates for the PHEVs range from approximately $3,500 to the full $7,500.[12]

That sounds like a great way to increase EV use and move us toward energy independence, encourage adoption, and help us compete with China's advancement in EVs. The problem: the original legislation put a cap on the tax credits by limiting them to 200,000 vehicles PER MANUFACTURER before a phase-out period begins. Both American automakers Tesla and GM hit the 200,000 vehicle threshold in 2018, meaning that in 2019 consumers will only see a tax credit of $3,750 in the first half of the year, and then a $1,875 credit in the second half of the year.

This threshold is the wrong approach because this disincentivizes manufacturers who took more risk and invested in electric technology upfront. First movers are actually at a disadvantage, as late movers won't hit the cap until much later. Furthermore, the two companies that hit the threshold are American automakers, so foreign automakers like VW, Toyota, and others will continue to benefit as the second movers push into the market.

We can fix that by removing the "limit per manufacturer," and put either a limit on the deadline (e.g., by 2030) or put a limit on the funds for the total program (e.g., $10 billion). Other countries also have it as a rebate instead of a tax credit, which means you get it immediately instead of having to wait until tax season to get the refund.

Luckily a bill has been introduced in Congress (HR 6274) called the "Electric Credit Access Ready at Sale Act of 2018" or the *Electric CARS Act of 2018* for short. The bill would remove the limit per manufacturer and instead change it to a ten-year limit. Additionally, it would remove the tax credit and replace it with a rebate, making it easier on the pockets of everyday Americans.[13]

Let's reward the innovators and early adopters, who took bigger risks. Let's remove the unnecessary limit per manufacturer on EV incentives for tax credits and instead move to a time-limited rebate to make it easier for Americans to purchase electric vehicles that help our country gain energy independence while helping Tesla and GM continue to dominate in the domestic EV market.

CARBON DIVIDENDS

Every Friday the city comes and picks up my trash, and I pay them for their services. Otherwise, neighborhoods and streets would be filled with trash, and eventually it would become a sanitary issue, similar to our society prior to waste management.

We should have similar standards for our air as well. When businesses and individuals put garbage into our air, they should be responsible for their waste. The difference between trash in the street and emissions in the air is that trash is local and doesn't impact other states or nations. Emissions, however, are global. US emissions impact China, and Chinese emissions impact the US.

In regard to climate action, times are a'changing on Capitol Hill. For the first time in a decade, a bill has been introduced by both Republicans and Democrats to address carbon emissions. If enacted, a price would be put on carbon, and the money would be returned to every American household in the form of a dividend check, which has been called Carbon Fee & Dividend (CF&D).

The original CF&D concept was embraced by the bipartisan advocacy group Citizens Climate Lobby (CCL) and by policy institute Climate Leadership Council (CLC)—yes the abbreviations are very similar. I've participated in CCL meetings, so I have a firsthand perspective on the group, which meets monthly and focuses on lobbying their members to join the bipartisan Climate Solutions Caucus and to endorse the CF&D model of addressing climate action. CCL has made significant progress in making climate action a bipartisan process, as the Climate Solutions Caucus had ninety members—forty-five Republicans and forty-five Democrats in 2018.[14] It's known as the Noah's Ark process, where a Republican and Democratic member must join together.

The CLC has been coined as the Baker-Schultz Plan, named after two prominent Republican statesmen. James Baker served as

Secretary of State under President George H.W. Bush, Secretary of the Treasury under President Reagan and White House chief of staff under both administrations. George Shultz served as Secretary of State under President Ronald Reagan and as Secretary of Treasury and Labor under President Nixon. On top of that, businessmen and economists are behind the plan as well, including:

- **Henry Paulson**: Secretary of the Treasury under President George W. Bush. Previously, he served as chairman and chief executive officer at Goldman Sachs.

- **Martin Feldstein**: Chairman of the President's Council of Economic Advisers from 1982 to 1984 under President Reagan.

- **Gregory Mankiw**: Chairman of the President's Council of Economic Advisers from 2003 to 2005 under President George W. Bush.

- **Thomas Stephenson**: Partner at Sequoia Capital, a venture capital firm based in Silicon Valley. Stephenson previously served as the United States Ambassador to Portugal from 2007 to 2009 under President George W. Bush.

- **Rob Walton**: Chairman of the board of Walmart, the world's largest retailer and employer, from 1992 to 2015. He is also currently Chairman of the Executive Committee of Conservation International.

Those are some big names behind this concept! On top of that, there are corporate founding members as well, including oil companies (BP, ExxonMobil, and Shell) and electric companies (Exelon and Schneider Electric).

In CLC's proposal, a family of four would receive $2,000 per month in year one, with 70 percent of Americans seeing a new benefit, according to the Treasury Department. For example, if a household received $2,000 a year, and their costs go up $500, they are still netting $1,500 more in their pocket. The worst polluting Americans will see their energy costs grow, mostly with their utility bill and at the gas pump, so the Americans with the biggest mansions and biggest SUVs—the people who can afford it the most—will see the greatest impact.

Dividends aren't a farfetched idea either, as citizens in Alaska get paid an oil royalty through an annual check from the Alaskan government. In 2018, Alaskan residents received a check of $1,600.[15] Now imagine this for every single household in America. According to the Department of Treasury, estimates show that 70 percent of Americans would benefit from carbon dividends.

The key proposal differences between various interest groups are the starting price of the carbon fee and the rate at which it grows annually. Below I present the various policies and bills.

TITLE	SPONSOR	$/TON OF CO2	GROWTH/ YEAR	100% DIVIDEND	NOTES
Carbon Fee & Dividend	Citizens Climate Lobby	$15	$10	X	
Carbon Dividends	Climate Leadership Council	$40	"steadily rising"	X	
Energy Innovation & Carbon Dividend Act	Rep. Ted Deutch	$15	$10	X	Bill has 9 cosponsors (3 Reps, 6 Dems)
Energy Innovation & Carbon Dividend Act	Sen. Chris Coons	$15	$10	X	Bill has 2 cosponsors (1 Rep, 1 Dem)
American Opportunity Carbon Fee Act	Sen. Sheldon Whitehouse	$49	2% over inflation		2 Dem cosponsors. Instead of dividend: reduce corporate tax rate; payroll tax credit; Social security & veteran's tax credit

A conservative might ask isn't this just a tax? No. There is a difference between a tax and a fee, depending on what the revenue is used for and typically who pays it. For taxes, money goes toward general governmental programs. For fees, money goes toward specific government programs or services. For example, the TSA fee on airline tickets is only paid by airline passengers, and the money specifically goes toward TSA services. On the opposite spectrum, I pay money each paycheck toward a payroll tax that goes into the Treasury's purse toward governmental services. Therefore, in this situation, it's a fee because the carbon cost will be paid by the polluters (fossil fuel companies)—and furthermore, the revenue goes toward a carbon dividend, rather than to the Treasury's purse for general services.

You might think that putting a price on carbon would negatively impact domestic businesses while Chinese companies can continue to smog up their cities. However, all of these proposals have a "carbon border adjustment."

Carbon Dividends will have a major positive benefit around the nation:

- **Americans**: Every American will have more money in their pocket to pay for food, rent, student loans, etc. Additionally, the movement away from dirty sources of energy will cut healthcare costs around the nation. The growth of solar will also continue to cut prices for rooftop solar, so households can power their homes through the sun on their roof.

- **Entrepreneurs**: The American scientists and innovators will see a market signal of the growth in cleantech going forward, meaning more innovation in clean energy and electric mobility.

- **Businesses**: Businesses in general make long-term planning decisions, so the economic certainty of what will happen with fossil fuels over the next several decades will create business certainty for long-term planning purposes. For example, transport-heavy companies like UPS are already investing in electric fleets, but their long-term decisions will get more aggressive, which will eventually lead to more orders to electric vehicle companies.

- **Utilities**: Our utility companies will move away from dirtier sources of energy, like coal, and move toward clean energy, like solar, wind, advanced nuclear, and storage. I also predict a war between fossil fuels and utilities will grow around the nation and on Capitol Hill. Utilities will greatly push for electric vehicles due to a rapidly growing revenue stream for utilities because of new electricity demand from the transportation sector.

- **Automakers**: A price on carbon will signal automakers to further their push on electric vehicles. Tesla is already 100 percent electric, but the domestic giants Ford and GM will further their focus on hybrid and electric vehicles domestically as they've already done in their Chinese strategy.

Many people will argue that this would never pass, but polling shows a different story. Both the Yale/George Mason and the Hill+Knowlton surveys show strong support for Carbon Dividends among Americans. The Yale/George Mason survey asked the following question: *"As you may know, some Republican party leaders have proposed requiring fossil fuel companies (coal, oil, and natural gas) to pay a tax on their carbon emissions and rebating all the money collected directly to all Americans through a monthly check. This proposed policy is called a "carbon dividend" because all households would receive a monthly cash dividend as part of an effort to combat climate change. Do you support or oppose this plan?"* Here were the results:

Opinion

- **Favor**: 58% (Strongly: 24%, Somewhat: 34%)
- **Oppose**: 23% (Strongly: 12%, Somewhat: 11%)
- **Unsure**: 21%

Party Lines

- **Republicans**: 62% favor, 20% oppose (and for Trump Supporters: 63% favor, 20% oppose)
- **Democrats**: 55% favor, 23% oppose
- **Independents**: 49% favor, 24% oppose[16]

A similar story comes from the Hill+Knowlton survey, where 56 percent favor Carbon Dividends. This survey looked at the younger generation as well (eighteen to thirty-four years old), where 71 percent supported the Carbon Dividends.[17] In fact, a student-led organization has launched at colleges around the US for this particular policy called the Students for Carbon Dividends, consisting of Republican, Democratic, and environmental campus groups. Many previous political movements have started with the younger generations, so perhaps Carbon Dividends will be one of the first climate policies we see enacted that will incentivize cleantech innovation in the US.

To push the political discussion on Carbon Dividends, Exxon gave $1 million to lobby for Carbon Dividends on Capitol Hill.[18] This is tiny compared to the $99 million in oil & gas lobby spending[19], but it's still a move in the right direction. The American support is there—we just now need the political will.

And in regard to China, you might think higher energy prices will put American businesses at a disadvantage, but the Carbon Dividends policy includes a solution called "carbon border adjustment," which will put an adjustment on imported goods as well as giving a refund for exported goods. This would mean that China's coal-heavy carbon-intensive economy would have a higher carbon adjustment as the goods enter the company, putting American businesses at a strategic advantage.

"Mounting evidence of climate change is growing too strong to ignore. While the extent to which climate change is due to man-made causes can be questioned, the risks associated

with future warming are too big and should be hedged. At least we need an insurance policy. For too long, many Republicans have looked the other way, forfeiting the policy initiative to those who favor growth-inhibiting command-and-control regulations, and fostering a needless climate divide between the GOP and the scientific, business, military, religious, civic and international mainstream. Now that the Republican Party controls the White House and Congress, it has the opportunity and responsibility to promote a climate plan that showcases the full power of enduring conservative convictions. Any climate solution should be based on sound economic analysis and embody the principles of free markets and limited government. As this paper argues, such a plan could strengthen our economy, benefit working-class Americans, reduce regulations, protect our natural heritage and consolidate a new era of Republican leadership. These benefits accrue regardless of one's views on climate science."

—TED HALSTEAD, CEO OF CLIMATE LEADERSHIP COUNCIL

For more information:

- Get background information about the Energy Innovation and Carbon Dividend Act at energyinnovationact.org.

- Watch the 2017 TED Talk by Ted Halstead entitled "A Climate Solution Where All Sides Win" on YouTube.

- Get involved in the movement with Citizens Climate Lobby by finding a chapter near you: citizensclimatelobby.org.

- Students can get involved on their campus with Students for Carbon Dividends: www.s4cd.org.

* * *

Tax reform has a big opportunity to influence the flow of money into cleantech and out of fossil fuels by providing tax cuts and credits for clean investments while putting a price on carbon. This will influence consumers, investors, innovators, corporations, and communities to make the right decisions by putting the right tax policies in place.

KEY TAKEAWAYS

- **Clean Tax Cuts (CTCs)**: CTCs are new tax policies that are slowly entering the national discussion and could influence the investments into clean energy, energy efficiency, and clean transportation projects around the US. For energy, proposals include Emission Reduction Bonds and Clean Asset Bonds to create tax-exempt corporate bonds for companies that are investing in clean energy and infrastructure. For energy efficiency, Reduced Clean Tax Rates can be applied to ENERGY STAR-rated buildings, and Clean Accelerated Depreciation can give tax advantages to investment in more energy efficiency projects. For transportation, CTCs could be applied to the current CAFE standards, where automakers would receive lower tax rates as they achieve more fuel-efficient targets.

- **Emerging Energy Credits**: Various tax credits exist for all forms of energy, including oil, gas, coal, solar, wind, and more. An emerging energy tax credit would provide technology-neutral tax incentives to new technologies, which phase out as energy production ramps up on the grid.

- **Master Limited Partnerships (MLPs)**: Oil and gas companies currently get to take advantage of MLPs, which has the tax benefits of a partnership, but is publicly traded. Fortunately, a Senate bill already exists called the MLP Parity Act, which would allow the financial structure to be available to all energy sources, not just to oil and gas. This can open up more investments in clean energy, like solar and wind.

- **EV Credits**: Ever since the 1973 Oil Crisis, we have been talking about energy independence, but over four decades later, we are still importing oil and gas from foreign countries. We can really bend the curve on foreign oil and advance our domestic market by enhancing our current EV tax credit. Issues with the current credit include a limited threshold, which has been reached by American automakers Tesla and GM. A bill already exists called the "Electric Credit Access Ready at Sale Act of

2018," which would remove the threshold, change it from a credit to a rebate, and end the rebate in ten years.

- **Carbon Dividends**: For the first time in a decade, a bill has been introduced by both Republicans and Democrats to address carbon emissions. If enacted, a price would be put on carbon, and the money would be returned to every American household in the form of a dividend check, called Carbon Dividends. The Energy Innovation and Carbon Dividend has been introduced in the House and Senate and is based off of policies pushed by Citizens Climate Lobby (CCL) and Climate Leadership Council (CLC). A survey conducted by Yale and George Mason found that 58% of Americans support a Carbon Dividend policy. In terms of global trade, the policy includes a carbon border adjustment on imports, putting American businesses at a strategic advantage compared to carbon-intensive countries like China.

CHAPTER 9

AMERICAN BUSINESSES

——

"Here in the land of technology leadership and free-market enterprise, American regulation has more than doubled the cost of solar."

—ANDREW BIRCH, FOUNDER AND FORMER CEO OF
SUNGEVITY, A SOLAR INSTALLATION COMPANY

We have scientists and entrepreneurs who are committing their efforts towards a Clean Revolution, but our outdated regulations have caused barriers for businesses, from small mom-and-pop solar companies to venture-backed nuclear startups. Our political leaders need to ensure that our regulations protect bad actors, but also don't hinder the majority of good actors.

In this chapter, we will discuss how cutting or revising outdated regulations can help move several clean technologies forward, like solar, nuclear, and hydropower, as well as implementing a nationwide energy network. These regulations increase the costs for businesses, which then are passed on to consumers. This not the only regulations we should consider, but this is a starting point for political leaders and regulators. In order to compete with China, we need to ensure our regulations are friendly for consumers, entrepreneurs, and businesses.

SOLAR

Imagine you are interested in putting solar on your roof, but it takes tons of time to make it finally happen. Our communities have the ability to cut the cost of solar in half, while also cutting the time of putting it on your roof in half as well, by eliminating redundant regulations that solar installers are required to comply with. A significant amount of the work in a solar roof project goes into complying with local permits and codes. Americans are paying a lot more for the same solar project than is found in other countries, such as in Europe, Asia, and Australia. Republicans and Democrats can come together and acknowledge that regulations for putting solar on your own roof are a bit too far for government involvement. Therefore, this issue is not only about fewer regulations, but it's also about consumer choice and private property rights for solar on your home.

We have seen this in the past, where government regulations for local codes were addressed at the federal level. A lot of rules used to exist around putting satellite dishes on your roof, which today is an easy installation process. But it wasn't always this way. Congress passed the Telecommunications Act of 1996, a broad bill making several changes to the telecommunications sector. One particular piece in the bill was around "Over-the-Air Reception Devices" (OTARD), which ultimately removed any restrictions on putting satellite devices on homes, which would violate the law if it: "(i) Unreasonably delays or prevents installation, maintenance, or use; (ii) Unreasonably increases the cost of installation, maintenance, or use; or (iii) Precludes reception or transmission of an acceptable quality signal."[1]

Andrew Birch wrote about the unnecessary regulations and compared solar installations in the US to those in Australia, his home country. Birch is the founder and former CEO of Sungevity, a residential solar company based in the US and Europe. He noted that in December 2017, it cost $1.34/watt to install a solar system in Australia, but it was $3.25/watt in the US.

One key reason for the difference is the permitting process in the US at the local level, which is estimated to add two to six months to the total solar installation timeline. It's a headache because the process requires (1) scheduling for a home visit, (2) a home visit with trucks and the resources needed, (3) an engineering drawing for the permit, and (4) finally an official submission to the permitting office, which is sometimes in person in some jurisdictions. Further time is required for any delays or if changes need to be made to the system, on top of calls to update the solar customer. Birch estimated that $0.47/watt could be removed from the total system cost with a change to the permitting process. The average residential solar system is 5 kW, meaning a $2,350 cost savings per install in labor, maintenance, and resources!

In the US, the US National Electrical Code requires specific practices that double the installation times and require additional hardware resources compared to Australia. In Australia, the Australian Clean Energy Council accredits installers, approves products, and has a voluntary code of conduct, making it easier for business to comply. By accrediting installers on a national basis rather than being nit-picky about each individual installation, the solar installation market can achieve great efficiencies in every project.

Delays in the solar installation can be costly to an installer, and the press release noted that a one-week delay due to permitting, inspection, or interconnection can lead to a 5–10 percent cancelation rate from customers, which ultimately increases costs for other customers. It is believed improvements could lead to a $7,000 reduction in solar costs for consumers.[2]

I recommend the US government consider legislation to reduce regulations, such as permitting and codes, for the implementation of rooftop solar, which will reduce consumers' costs, grow domestic jobs, and grow American solar businesses.

For more information, you can check out: https://www.thesolarfoundation.org/solarapp/.

HYDROPOWER

Hydropower has a special place in clean energy's history because it was America's first renewable energy source more than a century ago. Hydro accounts for 6 percent of electricity generation in the US, and the US has the third largest fleet of hydropower in the world.

Hydro also plays a unique role in the grid because in certain situations, hydro can generate electricity or also store energy. Electricity is generated by running water through turbines from higher elevations to lower elevations with the magic of gravity. But energy can also be stored by running that same water back up to higher elevations using a pump, hence the name pumped-storage hydro (PSH). As that water is pumped back to higher elevations, it is "stored" to be used at a later time when electricity is needed on the grid.

For example, in California, where solar is abundant, as the sun sets and solar generation ramps down, hydropower can help generate electricity. Also, if solar power is creating more electricity than is necessary for the grid, hydro can store that energy for the evening when the sun has set. Therefore, hydro is a power generator, yet it also functions as a battery if a pump is installed.

Hydro also has a special place for grid reliability. When the 2003 Northeast Blackout occurred that impacted eight states, hydro in western New York was able to put energy on the grid because it doesn't require an outside power source to kick start the process like other power sources do. The ramp-up capabilities of hydro provided grid reliability for the forty-five million people impacted by the blackout.[3]

First, America needs to work on upgrading our existing fleet of hydropower because the capacity-weighted average fleet age is fifty-six years, leading to one of the highest costs in upgrades per unit of energy compared to other nations. Over a decade (2007–2017), $8.9 billion in refurbishment and upgrade (R&U) projects occurred, with at least 223 turbines being installed across 93 plants. Furthermore, over a decade

(2006–2016), US capacity for hydropower has increased 2.0 GW for a total of 80.0 GW of hydro capacity, with 70 percent of the increase coming from R&U projects.

In DOE's Hydropower Market Report (2017), the authors noted that North America lags behind other regions, such as Europe and East Asia, in terms of new development of PSH. If you look at the table below, you can see that the US has a lot of PSH projects in the permitting and development stage, but none under construction, while the international community is ahead of us.

NUMBER OF PROJECTS (AND TOTAL CAPACITY) PER STAGE IN EACH REGION

REGION	PERMITTING & PLANNING	UNDER CONSTRUCTION	IN SERVICE (POST 2006)
North America	51 (21 GW)	0	1 (0.04 GW)
Europe	37 (16 GW)	7 (25 GW)	9 (4 GW)
East Asia	62 (75 GW)	26 (37 GW)	22 (26 GW)

Source: DOE 2017 Hydropower Market Report[4]

The authors noted that additional insight is needed to review the PSH authorization process and the available revenue streams for the various regions. With no projects under construction in North America, we need to work on moving projects forward in the process and address the regulatory structure we have in place in the US.

ClearPath, a conservative policy group, has put forward some ideas to ramp up hydropower in the US, relating to upgrading public dams, easing the regulatory process, and officially designating hydro as a renewable resource. Upgrading public dams is a great place to start because only 3 percent of the 80,000 dams in the US actually generate electricity. ClearPath recommends that the US Army Corps of Engineers (USACE) look into "electrifying" the top one hundred dams that are operated by USACE, which could lead to electricity for over a million homes and thousands of jobs. On top of that, USACE should also look into refurbishing, replacing, and updating existing dams, as the private sector spends three times more on dams than the public sector. Oak Ridge National Laboratory estimates that electrifying these non-powered dams can increase hydropower capacity by 15 percent.

Next, ClearPath recommends coordinating the federal review process, which can involve over a dozen federal agencies, such as FERC, USACE, EPA, NOAA, FWS, NPS, BLM, USFS, SHPO, THPO, and more, as well as potentially state and local agencies. Even a license renewal for a hydropower dam by California's Pacific Gas & Electric Company (PG&E) led to a cost of $20 million, even up to $50 million per project.[5] Furthermore, Cube Hydro Partners noted that licensing and permitting accounted for 25–30 percent of the project costs for a project in Pennsylvania.[6] Environmental studies can also be time consuming and therefore expensive. Congress should address how to ease the regulatory burden by streamlining the approval process and improving the environmental study process so we can increase hydropower projects across the US.

Finally, ClearPath argues that hydropower needs to be officially recognized as renewable energy, as the federal government is required to purchase 7.5 percent of their energy mix from renewable energy due to the Energy Policy Act of 2005, signed into law by President Bush. This would help influence the government purchase of hydropower. Furthermore, most energy sources have some type of tax credits, including oil and gas, solar, wind, and nuclear. However, in 2016, the tax credits for hydropower expired, meaning it's on an uneven playing field.[7]

I recommend the US government advance the upgrade and electrify our public dams, ease the regulation process, and designate hydro as a renewable energy source. Further development of hydropower will create more clean energy domestically, create more infrastructure jobs, and make America a leader in new hydropower construction again.

For more info about how we can effectively make progress in hydropower, you can check out ClearPath's policies: https://clearpath.org/policy/hydropower/.

ADVANCED NUCLEAR

Nuclear is sometimes the unloved stepchild of clean energy. The technology splits environmentalists apart, just like the technology splits atoms! It emits no pollution, but when people hear nuclear, they think mushroom clouds, Three Mile Island, and Chernobyl. People get irrational fear from nuclear, so we need to keep conversations separate regarding the old (existing nuclear reactors) and the new (the next-generation advanced nuclear). Concerns about nuclear typically evolve around the safety aspect of it due to disasters like Chernobyl and Three Mile Island. Over the last five years, coal power has led to 60,000 deaths, while automobiles have led to 250,000 deaths, yet we aren't nationally arguing to ban cars.[8] In fact, no one died directly from Three Mile Island incident although higher cancer rates have been seen in the area over the last several decades.[9] The risk of dying from a car accident is astronomically higher than death from a nuclear meltdown.

The reason I previously said that new nuclear is different than old nuclear is that nuclear meltdowns are typically caused by issues with the reactor's cooling system. The issue with nuclear reactors and water is similar to cooking pasta. When you are boiling pasta, the pasta itself only reaches boiling temperature (212°F) as the water boils and slowly evaporates off due to the energy from the stove. Sure, you can overcook the pasta, but the only way to *burn* the pasta is if the water evaporates out and you're just left with pasta in the pan.

The water supply is crucial for nuclear as well to keep from overheating. Numerous new designs for nuclear are being developed right now that have advantages over conventional nuclear. Molten salt technology removes the need of water for the nuclear reaction, which eliminates the risk of a major meltdown. The technology also produces less nuclear waste, meaning spent nuclear rods are less of an issue compared to conventional nuclear. The technology was originally designed by US scientists in the 1940s, and in 1956 the Oak Ridge National Laboratory began the development of a molten salt reactor power plant, which began construction in 1962. Unfortunately, in 1969, the Atomic Energy Commission (now the Department of Energy) canceled funding for the experiment.

Today, innovators are picking the technology back up. US-based TerraPower has been innovating in the US, but it eventually looked to China because the company "has found it remarkably challenging to build or secure access to the range of equipment, materials, and technology required to successfully commercialize its innovative design."[10] The nuclear company, which is financially backed by Bill Gates, recently announced that US restrictions on technology deals with China have caused the company to end the partnership with the state-owned China National Nuclear Corp.[11] Regulatory restraints and uncertainty are causing immense issues for American inventors and companies.

ClearPath, the same organization we discussed in the previous hydropower section, has put forth several nuclear policy reform concepts to help enable advanced nuclear in the US. Advanced nuclear is the next generation of this carbon-free technology, but development has been difficult in this regulatory environment. All existing nuclear plants use "light water" reactors, whereas newer nuclear designs are using technologies like fast neutron reactors and small modular reactors. Because of these technology changes, our federal government needs to implement regulatory changes as well. Below are ClearPath's three key policies to help advanced nuclear.

- **Reform the NRC funding model:** "America's nuclear companies pay for 90 cents of every dollar spent by the Nuclear Regulatory Commission (NRC). While cost-sharing keeps federal spending to a minimum, it also encourages the NRC to grow at the industry's expense. Instead, licensees and applicants should pay the NRC for activities specifically related to their operations, with Congress funding more general programs—such as the development of new regulations for the next generation of nuclear technologies. As was the case for the first generation of nuclear plants, some level of cost sharing for application review should also be provided."

- **Reform the NRC licensing process:** "Our country's nuclear permitting process is tailored to a single type of nuclear technology from the Eisenhower-era. The process, handled by the NRC, must be reformed because new nuclear technologies are coming down the development pipeline from top universities, national laboratories, and companies. Based on the old rules, new designs may be forced to add redundant features and face bureaucratic delays. The current system of licensing is so expensive and outdated that American advanced nuclear companies are looking to deploy their designs abroad. The nation needs to implement technology-neutral licensing processes so our best engineers develop their ideas here at home."

- **Share public resources:** "The private sector would benefit from greater access to the nuclear innovation facilities at our national laboratories and public research facilities. National laboratories already own expensive (and often underused) equipment that could significantly reduce private-sector development costs. Simply enabling the private sector to access national lab resources would lower costs and stimulate faster deployment times."[12]

I recommend the US government to review and update nuclear regulations to encourage the development of advanced nuclear innovation. As discussed in the first half of the book, China is pushing advanced nuclear technology, so we need to ensure that the right regulatory environment exists in the US to prevent scientists moving their nuclear designs to foreign countries. Advanced nuclear has the ability to scale up to meet the needs of the international community as they look to cleaner energy sources, but first we need to make the US an innovation test bed.

For more info about how we can effectively make progress in domestic innovation for advanced nuclear, you can check out ClearPath's policies: https://clearpath.org/policy/nuclear/.

A NATIONWIDE ENERGY NETWORK

You are able to drive anywhere in the US, mostly due to the highway system. You are able to find any information you want due to the internet. Now we need a nation-wide grid to connect windy and sunny areas with energy-heavy areas. Comparable to our body, we have multiple systems that work well when functioning – communication is handled through the internet and our nervous system, transport is handled through the highway and our circulatory system, and energy is transported through the grid and our digestive system. Systems are what keep our body and nation moving forward. We began building the grid at the end of the 19th century, and now we need to update it for the 21st century.

Building a 21st century grid is going to require a lot of jobs, just like the argument for fossil fuel pipelines today are all about jobs. The Keystone Pipeline, a pipeline planned to stretch from Canada to Texas, was a hot issue between Republicans and Democrats. The permit was denied by the State Department under President Obama, but it was ultimately approved under the Trump administration. The approval led Trump to say, "It's a great day for American jobs. Today, we take one more step toward putting the jobs, wages, and economic security of American citizens first."[13]

If giant infrastructure for fossil fuel pipelines is a big win for jobs, then giant infrastructure for a national electric grid will be a big win for jobs as well. A nation-wide energy network is necessary in order to connect windy and sunny regions to areas that are less fortunate with renewable sources. A key example is the amount of wind energy that is produced in the Midwest, but where the population density is much lower. Being able to connect a large quantity of wind energy to dense metropolitan areas in the coastal regions can help accelerate our transition to clean energy. Today our independent grids are outdated and insufficient. We need to connect the individual grids into larger networks between energy-rich areas and high-population cities using high-voltage direct-current (HVDC) transmission lines.

The arguments for direct current goes back to fight between Thomas Edison and Nikola Tesla on how to build the best grid. Most power lines near your home are transporting an alternating current (AC). AC works fine for short distances, such as the beginning of the grid, where many power stations were near homes. Direct current (DC) is much more efficient at long distances, by decreasing the amount of energy lost. It's easy to remember that DC is better for Distance. As the grid began, many power stations were put near where the power was needed. Now, we need a better ability to easily transmit energy long distances, and the best option is HVDC lines, similar to how oil and gas are moved long distances more efficiently through pipelines.

There has been a slow implementation of HVDC transmission lines due to opposition. Since these lines need to stretch vast distances, many of the problems come from right-of-way (ROW) issues, such as property disputes and permits for crossing waterways. Projects tend to get dragged in the dirt by lawsuits and regulations, which ultimately increase and even kill these large-scale projects.

A way to overcome these objections is by insulating the wires and burying them alongside roads, railways, and tunnels. These would remove many of the barriers that normally exist for overhead HVDC lines that may need to cut through private property.

A report released by Stanford gave several specific regulatory proposals that could help ease the advance of transmission lines across America:

"Congress granting FERC transmission siting authority like the agency has for natural gas pipelines; the Department of Energy making broader use of current authority it has in multiple states through its Power Marketing Administrations to site transmission lines, including eminent domain actions; implementing the 2015 federal FAST Act, discussed above, designed to accelerate and improve the cross-agency federal review and approval process for large infrastructure projects like transmission lines; strengthening the Energy-Right-of-Way Corridors Initiative under Section 368 of the Energy Policy Act of 2005; and simplifying cost allocation methodologies under FERC Order 1000."[14]

Jigar Shah, the cofounder and President of Generate Capital, also gave the idea to "direct the Department of Transportation to use federal highways to support HVDC lines or direct railways to use HVDC." The key issue is around finding right-of-ways for this "electric highway."

As we reach higher levels of solar and wind on the grid, we will eventually need to find a way to distribute those resources as a single network. Basic economics shows you need to match supply and demand, so let's create a way to match the energy supply to the energy demand. With an eventual 100% clean energy grid, HVDC lines are not an "if," but a "when." The quicker we can connect the various regions of America, the quicker we can move to a cleaner economy. America needs to build a federal interstate electricity highway. In my conversations with Katherine Hamilton, who is Partner and Co-Founder at 38 North Solutions in Washington D.C., she believes incentives around general transmission could exist in an infrastructure bill. Infrastructure bills are brought up frequently in Congress, so it could be an opportunity to move transmission projects forward. Political leaders in windy states would likely be interested in infrastructure projects in their states.

I recommend the US government consider regulatory reform and potential incentives to ease the implementation of transmission across the nation to form an "electric highway." A national global network will ensure that the clean energy supply meets the energy demand of our new clean economy.

* * *

Regulations are good at keeping out bad actors in many instances, but in terms of clean energy, overly burdensome regulations are blocking our transition to a clean economy. American politicians need to work with the clean energy community to see how regulations can be reduced to help the Clean Revolution flourish here in America. By reducing US regulations, we can help American innovators more effectively compete on existing and future clean energy technologies.

KEY TAKEAWAYS

- **Solar**: A significant amount of the work in a solar roof project goes into complying with local permits and codes. *I recommend the US government consider legislation to reduce regulations, such as permitting and codes, for the implementation of rooftop solar, which will reduce consumers' costs, grow domestic jobs, and grow American solar businesses.*

- **Hydropower**: Hydro accounts for 6 percent of electricity generation in the US, and the US has the third largest fleet of hydropower in the world. The US has a lot of PSH projects in the permitting and development stage, but none under construction, while the international community is ahead of us. *I recommend the US government advance the upgrade and electrify our public dams, ease the regulation process, and designate hydro as a renewable energy source. Further development of hydropower will create more clean energy domestically, create more infrastructure jobs, and make America a leader in new hydropower construction again.*

- **Advanced Nuclear**: Numerous new designs for advanced nuclear are being developed right now that have advantages over conventional nuclear. *I recommend the US government review and update nuclear regulations to encourage the development of advanced nuclear innovation.*

- **Transmission**: As we reach higher levels of solar and wind on the grid, we will eventually need to find way to distribute those resources as a single network. *I recommend the US government consider regulatory reform to ease the implementation of HVDC transmission across the nation to form an electric highway. A national global network will ensure that the clean energy supply meets the energy demand.*

CHAPTER 10

AMERICAN JOBS & COMMUNITIES

———

"We can no longer continue with a status quo energy policy. We must create sustainable clean energy jobs and leave the planet to our children and grandchildren in better shape than we found it."

—JEFF MERKLEY, US SENATOR FOR OREGON

EcoShot is all about the economic opportunity of the Clean Revolution, which will mean transitioning how we power and how we move about our communities. We can't transition our entire American and global economy without people in place to make that happen. The local benefits of the Clean Revolution will mean more jobs and cleaner air.

Polluting plants and vehicles will be a thing of the past, and clean energy and electric vehicles move us towards a sustainable economy.

Our federal government can play an important role in the implementation of existing and affordable cleantech solutions today by providing dollars to our communities around the country. The real cleantech action is going happen locally—in our cities, counties, and states. In the previous chapters, we focused on the policy angle, but this chapter will put forth the idea of massive grant potential allowing our communities to implement these cleantech innovations. In the first section, we will look at how to train and retrain Americans for the Clean Revolution. Second, we'll look at avenues for massive grants to retrofit buildings and provide clean energy in our communities. Third, we'll take a look at how we can clean up our streets by embracing electric municipal fleets, EV infrastructure, and mass transit.

The federal government can push cleantech adoption in states by providing block grants, which provide "blocks" of funding to state and local governments for projects. I recommend we use these block grants for job training, clean energy and energy efficiency implementation, and clean transportation to every state around the nation.

PART I: JOBS

The Clean Revolution is underway, so we need to train or retrain Americans to fill these clean energy jobs over the next several decades. As we see domestic jobs disappearing due to automation, offshoring, and outsourcing, we need to double down on creating jobs locally. Luckily, we already have some growing industries right now that can't be outsourced—in solar and wind.

According to the Bureau of Labor Statistics, the fastest growing occupations in America is solar photovoltaic installers (#1) and wind turbine service technicians (#2), paying a median salary of $39,490 and $53,880, respectively. On top of that, both jobs are expected to see a doubling in employment numbers in a single decade from 2016 to 2026.[1] Let's ensure the success of the Clean Revolution by training the American workforce.

JOB RE-TRAINING

As we transition away from fossil fuel use and toward clean energy, we need to realize the impact this clean energy transition will have disproportionately on communities. As the Director of Sierra Club's Beyond Coal Campaign says, "We must remember and honor the fact that our industrial age was built on the backs of coal miners in Appalachia. According to US Energy Information Administration, 70 percent of coal came from the top five states in 2016: Wyoming, West Virginia, Pennsylvania, Illinois, and Kentucky.[2] That means coal jobs are highly concentrated in our country. Clean energy jobs are bringing new jobs to communities across the country, but in these coal-heavy communities, it won't be enough to provide employment for everyone. We need to evaluate ways that our federal and state governments can help our fellow Americans, especially for those central communities that will be impacted the most by the clean energy transition.

Nonprofits are already aware of the issue and tackling it in the key coal states. Coalfield Development is a nonprofit organization in West Virginia focused on job training and economic development—a place where "Coal is King." It is known for its 33-6-3 model: 33 hours of paid labor, 6 hours of higher educational class time, and 3 hours of life-skills mentorship.

The thirty-three hours of paid labor is through one of the five social enterprises, which are described below. For the six hours of higher education classes, individuals are typically at the local community college taking classes. For the life-skills mentoring, personal development training can range from diet to balancing a checkbook. Coalfield started out as an initiative to help employment with young adults, but it soon expanded to help miners who had been laid off from their jobs.

According to the organization, they have been successful by creating "more than forty on-the-job training positions, more than two hundred professional certification opportunities, redeveloped more than 150,000 square feet of dilapidated property, and successfully launched five new businesses in real estate development, construction, wood working, agriculture and artisan trades—industries based on local assets and having real viability in the Appalachian region."

The organization is comprised of five social enterprises:

- **Reclaim Appalachia**: This business reclaims and revitalizes former mining sites. The sites are being turned into agroforestry projects and solar-powered aquaponics facilities. These projects are being tested and developed, with the hopes of scaling up for other areas in West Virginia.

- **Rediscovery Appalachia**: This business is focused on arts and culture, for the more creative types who like to be hands-on. An example is Saw's Edge Workshop, where crewmembers create a variety of home and business furniture and accessories for the region.

- **Refresh Appalachia**: This business not only trains locals for agricultural jobs, but it also helps farmers in the area by getting their produce into new markets, such as restaurants, hotels, schools, or grocery stores. There are also other unique projects such as putting a greenhouse on a rooftop.

- **Revitalize Appalachia**: This business creates green-collar jobs through sustainable construction projects. Projects can range from building a new apartment complex to restoring old buildings in the community.

- **Rewire Appalachia**: This business coordinates and implements solar projects for both homes and commercial buildings.[3] Robert Adkins, a crew chief, worked in coal for seven years but was laid off. He has now transitioned to working full time in solar.[4] He's still mining energy, but from above instead of below!

All of these individual enterprise units will interact on projects. Revitalize Appalachia might build a greenhouse for Refresh Appalachia. Much of the materials used to for these projects are repurposed from old factories and buildings in the region. Coalfield also works with local employers to match trainees with jobs and has a claim of 100 percent job placement. At the end of the program, trainees will have an associate's degrees, several professional certifications, paid work experience, and most importantly the confidence to find employment in the region.

For more information about Coalfield Development or how to make a donation, check out: http://coalfield-development.org/.

Related to impacted coal communities, the Partnerships for Opportunity and Workforce and Economic Revitalization initiative was formed in 2016 to revitalize the heavily impacted coal communities. The effort is a collaboration between the Department of Commerce (DOC), Department of Labor (DOL), Small Business Administration (SBA), and the Appalachian Regional Commission (ARC) while housed under the Economic Development Administration (EDA). Planning Grants are available to form comprehensive economic development strategic plans, and Implementation Grants are available to workforce development strategies.[5]

I recommend the US government expand grant opportunities under the existing POWER Program to provide job retraining and economic revitalization in the most heavily impact coal communities. We must ensure that American communities and American workers aren't left behind in this Clean Revolution.

CLEAN ENERGY JOB TRAINING

As noted in the beginning of the chapter, solar installers and wind technicians are the largest growing jobs. Grants to nonprofits focused on job training can play a big role around the nation. A model organization to check out is GRID Alternatives, which is the nation's largest nonprofit solar installer that benefits low to moderate-income communities while also giving hands-on experience to individuals. On the installation side, GRID Alternatives focuses on three groups: single-family homes, multifamily complexes, and community solar.

For the single-family homes, GRID installs solar systems at no costs to the low-income individuals while also cutting their electric bill up to 90 percent. Vicki McGill, a recipient of GRID's solar installation, said that a utility bill in the summer used to be $80, but with solar, it's now $4–5 dollars.[6] For the multi-family complex, GRID focuses on affordable housing providers by offering low-cost design and installation services to housing developers. Not all houses and buildings are ideal for solar, so community solar allows a homeowner or complex developers to take advantage of a solar project elsewhere while reducing their utility bills locally.

Not only do these installations help community members who need it the most, but they also provide technical training for job seekers. GRID has a hands-on program that allows individuals to choose between two certificate programs—Installation Basics Training (IBT) or Team Leader Training (TLT).

The organization has also partnered up with Wells Fargo to launch the Troops to Solar initiative, which provides training to military veterans and active service members. On top of the training, GRID also provides job connections by utilizing partnerships in the solar industry. Check out what John Janes has to say about the program below:

CASE STUDY—JOHN JANES, A MILITARY VETERAN

"Before I started the Troops to Solar internship, I never even considered solar installation as an option due to my inexperience in this profession. My belief was that it would be too difficult to learn the skill sets without having prior carpentry experience. When my Veteran's Affair job specialist initially brought this opportunity to my attention, I was excited yet also hesitant. He told me that I would be a good candidate for the position and he would vouch for me to be accepted. After a couple of days to think it over, I decided to make the commitment to learn solar installation and accept the opportunity to turn it into something beneficial for not just me, but others as well.

When I went to the GRID Alternatives website for the first time, I was happy to see that GRID extended their help internationally, as well as focusing their help on low-income families. The families getting solar installed were able to lower the cost of their electricity, as well as, introducing an environmentally safer way to power their home. I immediately started thinking of how useful solar could be in other countries, especially the less developed areas, such as the Philippines where I reside six months out of the year.

My first five weeks at GRID gave me a thorough classroom and hands on training in solar installation. I was amazed that I could be installing solar panels on roofs of actual homes. Meeting the homeowners gave me a sense of pride that I didn't expect. I learned so much, so quickly, and I gained confidence in areas that just a few weeks earlier seemed unthinkable. The staff here at GRID have been very supportive throughout the whole training process, from outreach and volunteerism, to the installations themselves. I look at my experience at GRID as a once in a lifetime opportunity. An opportunity that opens up to very promising directions."

SOURCE: GRID ALTERNATIVES – "AN OPPORTUNITY THAT OPENS PROMISING DIRECTIONS"[7]

Training is about giving both the experience and the confidence to make an impact in a growing industry. We need to ensure that the people who need jobs, such as low-income individuals and military members/veterans get access to jobs in the Clean Revolution.

For more information or donations to GRID Alternatives, check out gridalternatives.org.

ENERGY EFFICIENCY JOB TRAINING

They say "the greenest energy is the energy not used"! Therefore, we not only need new jobs in clean energy, but also new jobs in energy efficiency. Green Iowa AmeriCorps is a model organization that is focused on energy conservation in seven cities around the state of Iowa. The key role of corps members is providing energy audits, weatherization projects, and educational programs for the community.

With energy audits, the Green Iowa member will go to an individual's home, provide a free audit, and make recommendations on improving the home, such as patching up air leaks. This is done through a "blower test," which involves specialized equipment to evaluate potential air leaks throughout the home. At the end of the audit, a recommendation is made of the needed work and the associated costs.

Green Iowa members go through training and receive their Building Analyst Professional certification from the

Building Performance Institute (BPI). The Green Iowa AmeriCorps provides energy auditing training to its members while also helping the community in reducing utility bills by having more energy efficient homes.[8]

Green Iowa receives funding from a diverse group of organizations. The federal government provides funding through The Corporation for National & Community Service (CNCS), a federal agency that provides over a $1 billion in federal funding to various AmeriCorps programs around the country. Green Iowa also receives money from cities, universities, utility companies, and nonprofits in the area.

A CLEAN JOBS PROGRAM

As we've seen, communities are already beginning to find unique ways to help train individuals on a micro-scale. We can take this effort further by implementing a Clean Jobs Programs funded by our federal government but implemented by our local communities. Nonprofits have led the way in showing us a model for job training, but let's expand that nationwide in every corner of America. I spoke with Katherine Hamilton, who is cofounder and Partner at 48 North Solutions, and she believes there is a big opportunity as well for community colleges and technical schools to drive a national training initiative forward as well. She said, "Local governments and local organizations could get grants to implement programs, and the funding could be federal." She is also on the board of GRID Alternatives Mid-Atlantic, so she commented that nonprofits are mission-driven rather than money-driven, so it's important to have nonprofits as part of a jobs initiative.

We are constantly seeing and hearing about jobs going away due to automation, offshoring, and outsourcing. Imagine if we can implement job training programs for Americans who need it the most. Installing a solar panel on your roof can't be outsourced to China. Constructing a wind turbine in the Midwest can't be outsourced to Korea. Making your home more energy efficient can't be outsourced to Mexico. Let's put America back to work.

I recommend the US government provide job training and retraining to Americans across the country by administering block grants to states and organizations through the Partnerships for Opportunity and Workforce and Economic Revitalization (POWER) program and The Corporation for National & Community Service (CNCS). As we transition to a clean economy during the Clean Revolution, we need to make sure disadvantaged communities have access to these new jobs.

PART II: CLEAN ENERGY

In our state and local governments, many opportunities exist to implement clean energy and energy efficient projects, including low-income housing, fire and police stations, schools, libraries, water treatment plants, airports, and more. We can make significant progress by implementing clean energy and energy efficiency, which will be a gift that keeps on giving, as these projects will cut down the energy costs of our local governments. Several government programs and initiatives already exist, so the federal government should significantly increase funding for the various programs.

Energy efficiency is the cleanest (and cheapest form) of "clean energy," so governments should look to incorporate renewable energy, like solar, in combination with energy efficiency. The US government should push clean energy in our communities through block grants.

LOW-INCOME HOUSING

For low-income households, energy costs make up at 8.2 percent of their monthly budget, which is three times higher than higher-income households. Low-income households (LIHs) are estimated to include forty-nine million people, with income less than $40,000, accounting for 40 percent of households.

To weatherize the homes of Americans who need it the most, luckily we already have the DOE's Weatherization Assistance Program (WAP), which has weatherized over seven million homes in its forty-plus year history and is responsible for reducing energy costs for LIHs. Over one million homes came from the American Recovery and Reinvestment Act of 2009 (ARRA), which provided over $5 billion to the program. A national evaluation found that each project saved each household $283 or more on average in energy costs per year.[9]

WAP requires that all services are cost-tested by providing an energy audit and determining if the savings-to-cost ratio is 1 or greater, meaning that the costs put into the project will outweigh the energy savings. Since solar panel costs have dropped 50 percent from 2010 to 2015, WAP is now allowing solar to be included as part of their energy savings programs. The first retrofit plus solar project was done in 2016 in Colorado, where the house is expected to have net energy savings of $6,200 over twenty years.[10] Many financial barriers exist for the LIH population, as a George Washington University study found that less than 5 percent of LIH had solar installations.[11]

I recommend the US government provide significant increases for WAP, which could lead to significant jobs in solar and energy efficiency, grow our domestic cleantech industries, and cut energy costs for families who need it the most across the country.

MUNICIPAL BUILDINGS

As with residential homes, investments in municipal buildings with retrofits and renewable energy can provide significant energy cost savings. Government buildings tend to be large and trend toward being older, meaning we can make significant progress by retrofitting our state, county, and city government buildings. Let's take a look at how governments are saving both energy and money:

- **Municipal Buildings**: In Missouri, a city achieved significant savings. "Bemidji reviewed the proposed upgrades, and decided to complete work in eight city buildings, a wastewater treatment plant, street lighting, and vending machines. Upgrades included improving energy management systems, recommissioning direct digital controls, performing air leakage service, installing hot water high-efficiency modulating boilers, retrofitting lights with LED kits, and adding controls to shut down beverage vending machines when they were not being used. Due to the vendor competition during the bidding process, Bemidji was able to complete the projects under budget. The project has a combined annual energy saving of 15%, which will save the City $126,000 per year."

- **Community College**: Riverland Community College had 3 campuses that implemented energy efficiency programs — "The energy efficiency measures implemented across the College's facilities included lighting improvement, lighting controls, energy management controls, and building envelope. [...] Water conservation measures were added to the project along with upgrades to the theater's lighting, both of which would not have been possible with traditional financing. The energy efficiency upgrades reduced energy use by 27% and will save the College more than $136,000 per year."[12]

- **School Districts**: Kern High School District in California — "This 22 MW, privately financed project includes solar parking canopies on 27 district sites. The differential between the lower PPA rate and the higher utility rate is estimated to save the district $80 million over 25 years."[14]

Many energy efficiency projects are completed through an Energy Savings Performance Contracting (ESPC) by partnering with an energy service company (ESCO). The contract works by promising energy savings today while paying for the upgrades over the contract length. Government buildings are typically good candidates for ESPCs because of the long-term contract length available since the property is likely to stay in government hands for ten or more years. States have to obtain assistance and funding through the DOE's State Energy Program (SEP).

I recommend the US government provide block grants through SEP to states to encourage energy efficiency projects, which can be used toward ESPCs for government buildings or for other public benefits, such as hospitals, multifamily housing, or commercial buildings.

To further implement energy savings, block grants for rooftop solar development should be available as well. One stipulation is that buildings have to meet a certain efficiency standard before implementing solar, as energy saved is cheaper than clean energy. Also solar panels are typically matched to the energy demand, so reduced energy use would mean fewer solar panels needed.

For example, I discussed the community college that reduced 27 percent of their energy use. If the community college got enough solar to cover all of their energy costs, and then cut their energy demand by 27 percent, the system would be overproducing, which benefits the grid, but not the community college's pocket. We could see a one-two punch of energy savings by first implementing energy efficiency upgrades and then solar project deployment.

In some instances, rooftop solar isn't feasible, such as with taller, thinner buildings with little roof space, or it may not cover 100 percent of the energy need. Community solar is a solar project developed in a remote location, and the "subscriber" receives an energy reduction on their utility bill.

For example, in New York, Governor Andrew Cuomo announced its "Solar For All" initiative, which will build solar projects across the state, and low-income individuals will be able to participate, depending on their location, household income, and annual electric use. The President and CEO of the New York State Energy Research and Development Authority (NYSERDA) Alicia Barton said, "NYSERDA is proud to be advancing the Solar for All program to make sure that our most vulnerable residents have increasing access to renewable energy while supporting the Governor's commitment to lowering energy costs for New York families." The first round is expected to help seven thousand New Yorkers, with the second round in 2019 expected to bring the total to ten thousand.[15]

We should provide block grants to states through DOE's State Energy Program, so we can grow community clean energy projects for government and community buildings as well as low-income housing.

PART III: CLEAN TRANSPORTATION

The Clean Revolution is in the early stages for transportation, so we can do more to enhance the adoption in our cities, counties, and states. First, we will discuss how moving our government fleet to electric vehicles can actually lead to cost savings. Second, we'll discuss the need for more EV charging infrastructure to speed up the adoption of clean transportation. Finally, we will discuss advancing and innovating clean transit in our communities. The US government can provide block grants to states to accelerate this transition.

ELECTRIFYING MUNICIPAL FLEETS

Eco not only means environmentally friendly, but also eco-nomic sense. Electric vehicles have two key advantages: 1) the cost of electricity is much lower than gasoline, and 2) EVs requires less maintenance and therefore fewer costs over the lifetime of the vehicle. Those cost savings are important for local governments as well, who could have hundreds of vehicles in their fleets. The savings from the electrification of vehicles apply to city vehicles, public transit buses, and school buses.

The city of Seattle did an analysis on its fleet of three hundred sedans, finding $2 million in savings over ten years by switching to EVs. Seattle dove into the total cost of ownerships

(TCO), comparing a gas vehicle, a hybrid vehicle, and an electric vehicle.

REDUCED OPERATING COSTS

Vehicle Type	Life (yrs)	Acq.	Fuel (10y)	Maint. (10y)	Salvage	TCO	300 sedans
Gas (Ford Focus)	10	$21,284	$8,000	$11,790	$2,128	$38,946	*$11,683,800*
Hybrid (Ford CMAX)	10	$25,028	$5,830	$6,481	$2,503	$34,836	*$10,450,800*
BEV (Nissan Leaf)	10	$22,638	$1,980	$5,553	$2,264	$27,907	*$8,372,100*

Source: City of Seattle—"Fleet Electrification"[16]

A fully electric fleet of cars would save more than $2 million compared to a hybrid fleet and more than $3 million compared to a gas fleet over the ten-year life of the vehicle fleet. In a time when city, county, and state budgets are getting tighter, going electric might be a great way to tighten that belt and save taxpayers significant money. This is the cost savings for just one major city. Imagine if every city went electric… that could add up to hundreds of millions of dollars in savings. The story is the same for school bus fleets. Electric buses cost $120,000 more than diesel buses, but the lifetime fuel and maintenance savings are around $170,000 more for electric buses, giving a $50,000 lifetime savings.[17]

The US should push the needle on the transition by providing matching grants for cities around the US. Luckily, we already have the Congestion Mitigation and Air Quality Improvement (CMAQ) Program, which as the name suggests address air quality and congestion relief projects. Signed into law by President George H.W. Bush, the Clean Air Act Amendments of 1990 created CMAQ, which is housed under the Department of Transportation. In each region around the US, funds are administered by metropolitan planning organization (MPOs), which are federally mandated and federally funded transportation policy-making organizations.

I recommend the US government provide block grants through CMAQ to help transition municipal fleets to electric vehicles. Electric muni fleets will help push the electric vehicle market domestically, will cut down our foreign dependence on oil, and will clean up the air in our cities.

ELECTRIFYING AND ADVANCING PUBLIC TRANSIT

Electric buses: As we discussed in the first half of the book, China has become highly focused on zero emission buses (ZEBs). But now, the competition with the US is official—in 2016, US Transportation (FTA) Secretary Anthony Foxx and China's Minister of Transport Yang Chuantang announced a US-China Race To Zero Emissions (R2ZE) Challenge. A press release noted that it is "a collaborative and friendly competition that encourages cities and metropolitan transit districts in the United States and China to deploy innovative and advanced non-polluting Zero Emission Buses (ZEBs) in their transit systems."

The competition even has a target to have at least 35 percent of a city's fleet to consist of ZEBs by 2035. The Memorandum of Cooperation includes an annual meeting to announce the winning transit agencies.[19] Unfortunately, the dedicated FTA website for this initiative is no longer live,[20] so it can be assumed that it has been canceled by the new administration. That doesn't mean we should let China beat us in this Challenge.

In fall 2018, I attended the annual American Public Transportation Association's (APTA) Annual Meeting in Nashville. Two sessions were held around electric buses, and the rooms were packed wall to wall because public transit agencies wanted to learn more about the electric bus revolution and how to get involved. It had been a sleepy subject matter in past years, but this year, it was the new hot topic and a must-attend event.

There are nearly 1,100 public transit agencies across America with buses that use over thirteen million barrels of oil per year.[20] Cities and transit agencies are interested in electric buses, not only because they're cleaner but also because they now have major economic reasons. The Department of

Transportation has noted "electric buses have been observed to log 133,000 miles between maintenance compared to a CNG bus that averaged 45,000 miles between maintenance." Even though electric buses are costlier upfront, the maintenance costs are significantly lower over the life of the bus. Importantly, much of the capital expenditures for transit agencies, such as buses, are partially funded by the federal government.

Because the buses are much more expensive upfront but cheaper over the lifetime, the financial sector is getting savvier with how to fund these buses for agencies. Traditional leasing options are more difficult for new electric buses because traditional financial companies see the new technology as a risk. However, electric bus manufacturer BYD and financial firm Generate Capital created a partnership to make it easier for agencies to lease electric buses. Also, Proterra, a US-based electric bus manufacturer, is providing innovative financing by selling the bus near the cost of a regular bus, but the battery is leased, allowing the savings from maintenance to go toward the battery lease.

To advance electric bus adoption, we already have a program to get us there. The bipartisan *Low or No Emission Vehicles Program*, or Low-No for short, was passed under a Republican Congress and Democratic President in 2014. In 2018, the Federal Transportation Administration awarded $84 million in funding to fifty-two projects in forty-one states, which shows the high demand for electric buses across America.[21] The grant requires cost sharing with a non-federal match of 15 percent required for vehicles and can be used toward vehicles, facilities, charging equipment, or workforce development.

The transit industry is a case study example of the cleantech fight going on between the US and China. Chinese bus maker BYD has a manufacturing facility for electric buses in Los Angeles while American electric bus maker Proterra is based in Silicon Valley. BYD is backed by Warren Buffett while Proterra is backed by Kleiner Perkins Caufield & Byers, the famous firm that backed Amazon, Google, Twitter, and other prominent tech companies. Proterra CEO Ryan Popple predicts the entire bus industry will be electric in ten years, and I agree with him as the battery technology quickly advances.[22]

I recommend the US government enhance funding for the Low-No Program. America has a big opportunity to electrify our city buses, compete with Chinese dominance in electric buses, and clean up the air in our communities.

For more information about the Low-No program, check out https://www.transit.dot.gov/funding/grants/lowno.

Microtransit: With the rise of Uber and Lyft around the country, technology is transforming the transportation industry, including public transit. Consumers are now becoming accustomed to on-demand services, such as with ridehailing services. Mass transit is now looking to innovate by offering on-demand services using smaller shuttles—hence the name "microtransit." In large and medium cities, like Seattle or New York, large forty-foot buses can play a big role in moving a significant number of people around.

In areas where ridership is not high, cities and towns can implement microtransit—an on-demand service that includes ridegrouping. Whereas Uber is a private trip like a taxi, a microtransit rider might have other people on the shuttle—a publication has called it "Uber for Buses."[23] I work at TransLoc, a company that provides microtransit services to cities and transit agencies, who are looking to replace underperforming routes, serve new regions, connect people to existing transit routes, and more. If running a big bus doesn't make sense operating there, then microtransit can fill that service gap. The most interesting pilot is a town with the population of fifty thousand that had low ridership for their entire system, so the transit agency is working to transition its six transit routes into a fully on-demand service for the entire town. Cities have the ability to innovate as well in this Clean Revolution!

Innovation in mobility is not only about electrifying vehicles but also providing an innovative service like microtransit. I believe the real mobility revolution will come when transit adds autonomous technologies since the biggest cost to transit agencies is the drivers. The combination of Shared, Electric, Autonomous Microtransit will be called SEAMless mobility.

The ability to share rides will have massive impacts on getting cars off the roads in our major cities, and the removal of the driver will significantly cut operating costs. American companies are already innovating with SEAMless mobility, such as Local Motors testing out its Olli vehicle in cities around the US and around the world.[24] Over in China, Baidu, the Chinese equivalent of Google, announced in mid-2018 that it had started production of its autonomous bus, which will be tested out in Chinese cities with an eventual sight set on international markets.[25] A US-China innovation fight will grow in the SEAMless mobility space over the next decade.

I recommend the US government launch a SEAMless Mobility Program, providing grants to cities and transit agencies around the country to test out new technologies. These next-generation technologies would help push innovation and pilots around the country as well as incentivize American innovators to enter the market.

EV INFRASTRUCTURE

In our cities and on our highways, we need EV charging infrastructure to further the adoption of EV technology. Two federal agencies we have already discussed are already helping cities and states with these initiatives.

The previously mentioned CMAQ Program not only provides funding for government fleets, but the funds can also go to EV infrastructure for local governments. For example, North Florida Transportation Planning Organization used $300,000 in funding, in partnership with nonprofit utility JEA, to create a regional charging network with twenty-five stations.[26] Therefore, we have planning organizations in place for federal funding to local governments. This funding could be used not only for public charging infrastructure but also charging technologies needed for electric muni fleets and school buses.

For more regional transportation, like highways, states are working with the DOE's State Energy Program (SEP), the same program we mentioned earlier for clean energy. For example, in Nevada, the Governor's Office of Energy has a joint effort with the utility NV Energy to create EV infrastructure on Route 95, which connects Las Vegas and Reno. The state will leverage funds from SEP to offset installation costs. In the announcement for the project, Governor Sandoval said, "Electric vehicles are the wave of the future. I want Nevada to develop the infrastructure now to meet this developing technology."[27]

I recommend the US government provide block grants to advance charging infrastructure in cities through CMAQ and on highways through SEP. As EV adoption grows, we need to ensure a network is in place for EV drivers.

* * *

We can support American business and American workers around the nation by providing federal dollars through block grants to states for projects involving job training and retraining, clean energy and efficiency projects, and clean transportation. By ensuring a proper workforce and pushing implementation of clean projects around America, we can advance cleantech development like China.

KEY TAKEAWAYS

- **Jobs**: The Clean Revolution is underway, so we need to train or retrain Americans to fill these clean energy jobs over the several next decades. As we see jobs disappearing due to automation, offshoring, and outsourcing, we need to double down on creating jobs locally.

  - **Retraining**: As we transition away from fossil fuel use and toward clean energy, we need to realize the impact this clean energy transition will have disproportionately on coal-heavy communities. We should use the nonprofit Coalfield Development as a prime example of economic development in these communities. *I recommend* *the US government expand grant opportunities under the existing POWER Program to provide job retraining and economic revitalization in the most heavily impacted coal communities. We must ensure that American communities and American workers aren't left behind in this Clean Revolution*

- **Clean Jobs Program**: Nonprofits around the country are providing job training in clean energy and energy efficiency, like GRID Alternatives and Green Iowa AmeriCorps, which we should replicate on a wider scale. *I recommend the US provide job training and retraining to Americans across the US by administering block grants to states and organizations through the Partnerships for Opportunity and Workforce and Economic Revitalization (POWER) program and The Corporation For National & Community Service (CNCS). As we transition to a clean economy during the Clean Revolution, we need to make sure disadvantaged communities have access to these new jobs.*

- **Clean Energy**: In our state and local governments, many opportunities exist to implement clean energy and energy efficient projects, including low-income housing, fire and police stations, schools, libraries, water treatment plants, airports, and more.

- **Low-Income Households**: Energy costs make up at 8.2 percent of the monthly budget for low-income households, which is three times higher than higher-income households. *I recommend the US government provide significant increases for Weatherization Assistance Program (WAP), which could lead to significant jobs in solar and energy efficiency, grow our domestic cleantech industries, and most importantly, cut energy costs for families that need it the most.*

- **Municipal Buildings**: Investments in municipal buildings with retrofits and renewable energy can provide significant energy cost savings. Government buildings tend to be large and trend toward being older, meaning we can make significant progress by retrofitting our state, county, and city government buildings. *I recommend the US government provide block grants through SEP to states to encourage energy efficiency and clean energy projects for government buildings or for other public benefits, such as hospitals, multifamily housing, or commercial buildings.*

- **Clean Transportation**: The Clean Revolution is in the early stages for transportation, so we can do more to enhance the EV adoption in our cities, counties, and states.

  - **Government Fleet**: Electric vehicles have the economic advantage of lower fuel and maintenance costs, meaning

significant savings over the lifetime of the vehicle. *I rec-*
ommend the US government provide block grants through
CMAQ to help transition municipal fleets to electric vehi-
cles. Electric muni fleets will help push electric vehicle mar-
ket domestically, will cut down our foreign dependence on
oil, and will clean up the air in our cities.

- **Public Transportation**: Even though electric buses are
  costlier upfront compared to diesel buses, the fuel and
  maintenance costs are significantly lower over the lifetime of the bus. *I recommend the US government enhance*
  funding for the Low-No Program. America has a big oppor-
  tunity to electrify our city buses, compete with Chinese
  dominance in electric bus, and clean up the air in our com-
  munities. Furthermore, the transit agency is innovating
  by adopting more on-demand ridegrouping services, or
  "Uber for buses." As various innovations converge, the
  ultimate shift will happen with Shared, Electric, Autonomous Microtransit mobility, or better called SEAM-
  less mobility. *I recommend the US government launch a*
  SEAMless Mobility Program, providing grants to cities and
  agencies around the country to test out new technologies.
  These next-generation technologies would help push inno-
  vation and pilots around the country, as well as incentivize
  American innovators to enter the market.

- **Charging Infrastructure**: In our cities and on our highways, we need EV charging infrastructure to further the adoption of EV technology. *I recommend the US government provide block grants to advance charging infrastructure in cities through CMAQ and on highways through SEP.*

CHAPTER 11

PAYING FOR THE FOUR PILLARS OF CLEANTECH

"The clear and present danger of climate change means we cannot burn our way to prosperity. We already rely too heavily on fossil fuels. We need to find a new, sustainable path to the future we want. We need a clean industrial revolution."

—BAN KI-MOON, THE EIGHTH SECRETARY-
GENERAL OF THE UNITED NATIONS (2007-2016)

In the second half of the chapter, I do a recap of all of the policies I covered in the book in "cheat sheet," but first I must touch on one important topic. I have a family friend who lobbies to Congressional members, and he said "you better talk how to pay for it in your book." If the nation started taking action in the late 1980s when climate change was first being discussed in Congress, we could've made incremental changes in innovation and policies to make us a world leader in the next industrial revolution, but instead China made the investments yesterday to advance their industries in being an industry leader today.

The first place to look for an EcoShot is to end the permanent federal subsidies that oil and gas have enjoyed for decades. Today, fossil fuels companies get over $14.6 billion per year in federal subsidies: $10.9 billion go to oil and gas companies, and $3.7 billion go to coal companies. If we want to lead the next industrial revolution, we can't give a financial advantage to the mature energy sources of the last industrial revolution.

SUBSIDY DESCRIPTION	AMOUNT ($M)	BENEFIT
Intangible drilling cost deduction	2,292	Oil & Gas
Last-in, first-out accounting	1,690	Oil & Gas
MLPs corporate tax exemption	1,614	Oil & Gas
Excess of % over cost depletion	1,310	Oil & Gas
Lost royalties on deep water drilling	1,072	Oil & Gas
Low-cost leasing in Powder River Basin	963	Coal
Domestic manufacturing deduction	805	Oil & Gas
Fossil fuel R&D	591	Oil, Gas & Coal
Dual capacity taxpayer deduction	530	Oil & Gas
Amortization for coal pollution control	450	Coal
Other	3,393	Oil, Gas & Coal
TOTAL	$14,710	

Source: Oil Change International — "Dirty Energy Dominance: Dependent on Denial"

I could spend an entire chapter going through every single subsidy, but I'm not here to put you to sleep. Also, if you look at permanent tax credits for both fossil fuels and clean energy, fossil fuels still beat out in government handouts by a 7:1 margin.[1]

Furthermore, a noteworthy point is that the cost of fossil fuels does not include indirect military costs associated with protecting oil shipping routes across the globe. Securing America's Future Energy (SAFE), an organization that looks at the national security risk of America's oil dependence, did an analysis and found that **$81 billion** is spent every year on defending oil supplies. Last time I passed by a wind or solar farm, I didn't see any military bases or American soldiers there. The report noted that the subsidy was equivalent to a subsidy of $0.28 per gallon of fuel.* With nearly $15 billion in subsidies from the federal government and $80 billion in subsidies from military protection, we are wasting and subsidizing the fossil fuel with almost $100 billion a year.

Lobbying by fossil fuels companies have paid off significantly. According to a report by Oil Change International (OCI), "in the 2015-2016 election cycle, oil, gas, and coal companies spent $354 million in campaign contributions and lobbying and received $29.4 billion in federal subsidies in total over those same years — an 8,200% return on investment."[2] That's a pretty hefty return on investment.

Furthermore, if you look at the potential cost of climate change with no action, the downside risk is immense. The most recent National Climate Assessment (NCA) released in late 2018 reviewed the various impacts of climate change on infrastructure, agriculture, health, communities, the economy, and more. In the summary findings around the impact on US economy, the report stated "With continued growth in emissions at historic rates, annual losses in some economic sectors are projected to reach hundreds of billions of dollars by the end of the century —more than the current gross domestic product (GDP) of many U.S. states."[3]

SECTOR	ANNUAL DAMAGES UNDER RCP8.5
Labor	$155B
Extreme Temperature Mortality	$141B
Coastal Property	$118B
Air Quality	$26B
Roads	$20B
Electricity Supply & Demand	$9B
Inland Flooding	$8B
Urban Drainage	$6B
Rail	$6B
Water Quality	$5B
Coral Reefs	$4B
West Nile Virus	$3B
Freshwater Fish	$3B
Winter Recreation	$2B
Bridges	$1B
Munic. & Industr. Water Supply	$316m
Harmful Algal Blooms	$199m

Alaska Infrastructure	$174m
Shellfish	$23m
Agriculture	$12m
Aeroallergens	$1m
Wildfire	-$106m

Source: Fourth National Climate Assessment report

Climate change isn't just an environmental issue, as it's also a significant economic issue. Therefore, the real question is *what happens if we do not implement an EcoShot.* As the NCA report noted, climate change could have annual impacts of hundreds of billions of dollars by the end of the century. The report was originally signed into law by President George H.W. Bush through the The Global Change Research Act of 1990 in order to give an update on the impact of climate change to political leaders every 4 years. Therefore, our political leaders should listen to 1,515-page analysis that is telling us that inaction will be extremely costly to our nation. "RCP8.5" in the graph is the representative of the "higher scenario" with "higher population growth, less technological innovation, and higher carbon intensity of the global energy mix." Therefore, we have the ability to prevent this scenario, but it will require immediate and massive action by our political leaders.

The cost of climate change is similar to healthcare, as prevention is cheaper than treatment. It's cheaper to prevent skin cancer through frequent check ups than paying for late-stage skin cancer treatment due to inaction. Also the earlier we treat

the disease, the higher the probability of better future outcomes. The cost of action right now is substantially less than
what we will pay if we don't act. We can pay for an EcoShot to
transition America to a clean economy and be a world leader
in the Clean Revolution. Or we can continue to "kick the can"
down the road by arguing how to pay for it, while the future
debt to our children and nation grows every single day.

Let's transition our economy away from fossil fuels to create
a clean economy. The richest and most powerful nation in the
world has the ability to implement America's EcoShot — now
we just need the willpower.

* * *

Below is the recap of my recommendations included in the
4 Pillars of CleanTech Policy that will push innovation and
implementation of clean energy and clean transportation
around America.

PILLAR 1: AMERICAN SCIENTISTS

- **Innovation Grants**: The Department of Energy's (DOE)
  Advanced Research Projects Agency-Energy (ARPA-E), which
  was modeled after Department of Defense's (DOD) DARPA
  program, would be a perfect avenue for rapidly expanding
  R&D efforts in the United States, helping our country compete

with China. The US had great success as a part of its SunShot Initiative, which had a goal to bring down the cost of residential and utility-scale solar energy. We should expand this program to look at 10 areas of innovation, putting $1 billion in each area of innovation, including, but not limited to, technologies in: solar, wind, geothermal, hydropower, energy storage, carbon capture, next-generation nuclear, next-gen fuels (hydrogen fuel cells and biofuels), efficient appliances, and grid technologies. Right now, the current budget of ARPA-E is around $300 million, but we should significantly expand this funding to $10 billion to help America become the leader in cleantech innovation.

- **Implementation Loans**: as we see feasible technologies come out of our research, we need to provide financial opportunities for our businesses when they reach the *Valley of Death*. Through the DOE's Loan Program Office, we can provide loans to businesses that need to deploy new innovations at a large-scale. Energy innovation is an infrastructure, which requires significant capital to move beyond the research & development stage.

PILLAR 2: AMERICAN INVESTORS

- **Clean Tax Cuts** (CTCs): CTCs are new tax policies that are slowly entering the national discussion that could influence the investments into clean energy, energy efficiency, and clean transportation projects around the US. For energy, proposals include Emission Reduction Bonds and Clean Asset Bonds to create tax-exempt corporate bonds for companies who are investing in clean energy and infrastructure. For energy efficiency, Reduced Clean Tax Rates can be applied to ENERGY STAR-rated buildings, and Clean Accelerated Depreciation can give tax advantages to investment in more energy efficiency projects. For transportation, CTCs could be applied to the current CAFE standards, where automakers would receive lower tax rates at they achieve more fuel-efficient targets.

- **Emerging Energy Credits**: various tax credits exist for all forms of energy, including oil, gas, coal, solar, wind, and more. An emerging energy tax credit would provide technology-neutral tax incentives to new technologies, which phase out as energy production ramps up on the grid.

- **Master Limited Partnerships** (MLPs): Oil & gas companies currently get to take advantage of MLPs, which has the tax benefits of a partnership, but is publicly traded. Fortunately, a Senate bill already exists called the MLP Parity Act, which would allow the financial structure to be available all energy sources, not just to oil and gas. This can open up more investments in clean energy, like solar and wind.

- **EV Credits**: ever since the 1973 Oil Crisis, we have been talking about energy independence, but over 4 decades later, we are still importing oil and gas from foreign countries. We can bend the curve on foreign oil and advance our domestic market by enhancing our current EV tax credit. Issues with the current credit include a limited threshold, which has been reached by American automakers Tesla and GM. A bill already exists called the "Electric Credit Access Ready at Sale Act of 2018," which would remove the threshold, change it from a credit to a rebate, and end the rebate in 10 years.

- **Carbon Dividends**: For the first time in a decade, a bill has been introduced by both Republicans and Democrats to address carbon emissions. If enacted, a price would be put on carbon, and the money would be returned to every American household in the form of a dividend check, called Carbon Dividends. The Energy Innovation and Carbon Dividend has been introduced in the House and Senate and is based off of policies pushed by Citizens Climate Lobby (CCL) and Climate Leadership Council (CLC). A survey conducted by Yale and George Mason found that 58% of Americans support a Carbon Dividend policy. In terms of global trade, the policy includes a carbon border adjustment on imports, putting American businesses at a strategic advantage compared to carbon-intensive countries like China.

PILLAR 3: AMERICAN BUSINESSES

- **Solar**: Significant amount of work in a solar roof project goes into complying with local permits and codes. *I recommend that the US government consider legislation to reduce regulations, such as permitting and codes, for the implementation of rooftop solar, which will reduce consumers costs, grow domestic jobs, and grow American solar businesses.*

- **Hydropower**: Hydro accounts for 6 percent of electricity generation in the US, and the US has the third largest fleet of hydropower in the world. US has a lot of PSH projects in the permitting and development stage, but none under construction, while the international community are ahead of us. *I recommend the US government advance the upgrade and electrify our public dams, ease the regulation process, and designate hydro as a renewable energy source. Further development of hydropower will create more clean energy domestically, create more infrastructure jobs, and make America a leader in new hydropower construction again.*

- **Advanced Nuclear**: Numerous new designs for advanced nuclear are being developed right now that have advantages over conventional nuclear. *I recommend the US government to review and update nuclear regulations to encourage the development of advanced nuclear innovation.*

- **Transmission**: As we reach higher levels of solar and wind on the grid, we will eventually need to find way to distribute those resources as a single network. *I recommend the US government to consider regulatory reform to ease the implementation of HVDC transmission across the nation to form an electric highway. A national global network will ensure that the clean energy supply meets the energy demand.*

PILLAR 4: AMERICAN JOBS & COMMUNITIES

- **Jobs**: The Clean Revolution is underway, so we need to train or retrain Americans to fill these clean energy jobs over the several next decades. As we see jobs disappearing from automation, offshoring, and outsourcing, we need to double down on creating jobs locally.

  - **Retraining**: As we transition away from fossil fuel use and toward clean energy, we need to realize the impact that this clean energy transition will have disproportionately on coal-heavy communities. We should use the nonprofit Coalfield Development as a prime example of economic development in these communities. *I recommend the US government to expand grant opportunities under existing* **POWER Program** *to provide job retraining and economic revitalization in the most heavily impact coal communities. We must ensure that American communities and American workers aren't left behind in this Clean Revolution*

- **Clean Jobs Program**: Nonprofits around the country are providing job training in clean energy, like GRID Alternatives, and in energy efficiency, like Green Iowa AmeriCorps, which we should replicate around the country. *I recommend the US provide job training and retraining to Americans across the US by administering block grants to states and organizations through the Partnerships for Opportunity and Workforce and Economic Revitalization (POWER) program and The Corporation For National & Community Service (CNCS). As we transition to a clean economy during the Clean Revolution, we need to make sure disadvantaged communities have access to these new jobs.*

- **Clean Energy**: In our state and local governments, many opportunities exist to implement clean energy and energy efficient projects, including low-income housing, fire and police stations, schools, libraries, water treatment plants, airports, and more.

  - **Low-Income Households**: Energy costs make up at 8.2 percent of monthly budget for low-income households, which is 3 times higher than non-low-income households. *I recommend the US government provide significant increases for Weatherization Assistance Program (WAP), which could lead to significant jobs in solar and energy efficiency, grow our domestic cleantech industries,* *and, most importantly, cut energy costs for families that need it the most.*

- **Municipal Buildings**: Investments in municipal buildings with retrofits and renewable energy can provide significant energy cost savings. Government buildings tend to be large and trend toward being older, meaning we can make significant progress by retrofitting our state, county, and city government buildings. *I recommend the US government provide block grants through SEP to states to encourage energy efficiency and clean energy projects for government buildings or for other public benefits, such as hospitals, multifamily housing, or commercial buildings.*

- **Clean Transportation**: The Clean Revolution is in the early stages for transportation, so we can do more to enhance the EV adoption in our cities, counties, and states.

  - **Government Fleet**: Electric vehicles have the economic advantage of lower fuel and maintenance costs, meaning significant savings over the lifetime of the vehicle. *I recommend the US government provide block grants through CMAQ to help transition municipal fleets to electric vehicles. Electric muni fleets will help push electric vehicle market domestically, will cut down our foreign dependence on oil, and will clean up the air in our cities.*

- **Public Transportation**: Even though electric buses are costlier upfront compared to diesel buses, the fuel and maintenance costs are significantly lower over the lifetime of the bus. *I recommend the US government enhance funding for the Low-No Program. America has a big opportunity to electrify our city buses, compete with Chinese dominance in electric bus, and clean up the air in our communities.* Furthermore, the transit agency is innovating by adopting more on-demand ridegrouping services, or "Uber for buses." As various innovations converge, the ultimate shift will happen with Shared, Electric, Autonomous Microtransit mobility, or better called SEAMless mobility. *I recommend the US government launch a SEAMless Mobility Program, providing grants to cities and agencies around the country to test out new technologies. These next-generation technologies would help push innovation and pilots around the country, as well as incentivize American innovators to enter the market.*

- **Charging Infrastructure**: In our cities and on our highways, we need EV charging infrastructure to further the adoption of EV technology. *I recommend the US government provide block grants to advance charging infrastructure in cities through CMAQ and on highways through SEP.*

EPILOGUE

———

The Clean Revolution will be the greatest economic opportunity over the next several decades, as the world transitions to a clean economy. China has led its domestic innovation through massive R&D funding, incentives, subsidies, and mandates. Even though China is the world's largest emitter, it's also the world's biggest cleantech investor. I hope this book will be a wakeup call for Americans and US governmental leaders to finally embrace clean technologies, so the US can be a global innovator, rather than cede leadership to China. In my honest opinion, I believe China will win the Clean Revolution unless we have a national EcoShot that is embraced by both sides of the aisle. China's domestic push for next generation technologies in energy and transportation will continue to drive down prices, which will make Chinese businesses highly competitive in the international market, as it has already accomplished with solar and wind energy. China's Belt and Road Initiative will advance strategic allies over the coming decades, which will allow the Asian powerhouse to both finance and implement clean energy projects globally. We can also expect to see Chinese companies enter the US market, as we've already seen with electric bus manufacturers and solar companies.

If the US government supports a bold cleantech agenda behind innovation, incentives, and implementation, we might achieve a buzzer-beater win against China. But time is of the essence for catching up on innovation before we are too far behind. We have the smartest minds, the top universities, and the best research labs in the world, but American political leadership must give the right market signals and pass the effective policies to move the nation in a unified direction—toward a Clean Revolution led by America. As the futurist Roy Amara famously said, "We tend to overestimate the effect of a technology in the short run and underestimate the effect in the long run."

The timing for this book has been very interesting, as for the first time in a decade, bipartisan legislation has been introduced to address carbon emissions—the Energy Innovation and Carbon Dividends Act. We still bold action to get political leadership behind it, but the cracks are breaking in the political dam. Carbon Dividends would be the first step in moving our economy away from fossil fuels by placing a price on carbon, which would also incentivize entrepreneurs and businesses to invest in clean technologies.

The other timely event was the political movement brought on by the youth-led Sunrise Movement, who has now put a "Green New Deal" at the top of the Democratic platform. Dozens of young advocates filled the halls of Capitol Hill and Congressional offices to ask for action on climate change by requesting a Select Committee on Climate Change, which was last established in 2007. The original New Deal by President Roosevelt consisted of a series of government programs and projects that focused on the 3 R's: relief for the unemployed and poor, recovery of the economy during the Great Depression, and a reform to prevent another financial disaster. The evolving Green New Deal aims to promote job growth through a socially just Job Guarantee Program and reform our fossil-fuel economy to a renewable energy economy.

If you asked me at the beginning of 2018 if bipartisan climate solutions would be introduced in 2018 and that climate would be a priority for the House in 2019, I would have laughed out loud. Luckily, we have people advocating for climate solutions around the country, both young and old. I would like to thank Citizens Climate Lobby members for strongly pushing for Carbon Dividends legislation and the Sunrise Movement youth for making climate change a policy priority. We finally have an opportunity to cut carbon emissions, innovate in cleantech, and clean up our communities and our planet.

A GRAND ALLIANCE

The future of cleantech now relies on the nation's largest public-private-people partnership. We need public capital (government policies and funding), private capital (corporate innovation and funding), and social capital (advocacy).

The social capital piece involves you. If you want to personally contribute to the movement, here are a few recommendations:

- **Volunteer**: In the book, we have spoken about Citizen Climate Lobby, but other environmental groups like 350.org, Sierra Club, and the Climate Reality Project also have local chapters around the country. Religious-related environmental groups also exist, such as the Interfaith Power & Light. I tried out several groups to see which fits my personality, so you should do the same.

- **Donate**: Some people prefer to give money instead of their time. Consider donating to one of the groups previously mentioned. Some environmental organizations are also focused on action at the national level, like the Environmental Defense Fund, National Resources Defense Fund, The Nature Conservancy, World Wildlife Fund, and Greenpeace. A small, recurring donation can make a difference—$10 per month means $120 a year.

- **Advocate**: Frequently call your local, state, and federal representatives to advocate for climate action and investments in energy innovation.

    - **EcoApp**: To help advocacy efforts across the nation, I'm launching EcoApp, a mobile app platform to make it easier for American citizens to advocate for climate solutions by calling our local, state, and national political leaders. Innovation is disrupting our energy system, and now it's time for innovation to disrupt advocacy. Check out EcoApp at www.ecoshot.org/ecoapp to join the movement to transform our political system for a better future.

To really push this movement forward, we need to bring stakeholders together and put our collective voices behind a select policy changes. As individuals, we will achieve incremental changes, but as a collective group, we can make significant progress on climate action. I'm calling for an EcoAlliance of advocates, nonprofits, think tanks, academic scholars, policy wonks, and financiers to collectively push climate solutions. We need collective action to embrace a national EcoShot.

Let's create millions of jobs while transitioning our American society to a clean economy. Let's push our political leaders to make ambitious plans and policies for cleantech and the Clean Revolution, in order to provide a better future for their constituents and not their donors. Let's transform the world by coming together for a cause that positively impacts us, our children, and generations to come. Let's launch an EcoShot.

REFERENCES

INTRODUCTION

1. "Five Things You Didn't Know About Energy In China (VIDEO)".
   2017. *Nexus Media*. Accessed January 17 2019. https://nexusmedianews.com/
   five-things-you-didnt-know-about-energy-in-china-video-b86f202169d1?gi=51d375df6d52.

2. "Why China Wants To Lead On Climate, But Clings To Coal (For Now)". 2019. *NYTimes.com*.
   Accessed January 17 2019. https://www.nytimes.com/2017/11/14/climate/china-coal.html.

CHAPTER 1: THE NEXT INDUSTRIAL REVOLUTION

1. "Solar Costs Now Lower Than Coal And Even Natural Gas". 2019. *SEIA*. Accessed January
   17 2019. https://www.seia.org/blog/solar-costs-now-lower-coal-and-even-natural-gas.

2. "California Just Adopted Its Boldest Energy Target Yet: 100%
   Clean Electricity". 2018. *Vox*. Accessed January 17 2019. https://
   www.vox.com/energy-and-environment/2018/8/31/17799094/
   california-100-percent-clean-energy-target-brown-de-leon.

3. "Electric Vehicle Battery: Materials, Cost, Lifespan". 2019. *Union Of Concerned Scientists*.
   Accessed January 17 2019. https://www.ucsusa.org/clean-vehicles/electric-vehicles/elec-
   tric-cars-battery-life-materials-cost#.XD_-m89KhQJ.

4.   "Electric Cars May Be Cheaper Than Gas Guzzlers in Seven Years". 2018. *Bloomberg.
     com*. Accessed January 17 2019. https://www.bloomberg.com/news/articles/2018-03-22/
     electric-cars-may-be-cheaper-than-gas-guzzlers-in-seven-years.

5.   Grinshpun, Michael. 2018. "Tesla Model 3 = #1 Best Selling Car In The US (In Reve-
     nue)". *Cleantechnica*. Accessed January 17 2019. https://cleantechnica.com/2018/09/09/
     tesla-model-3-becomes-1-best-selling-car-in-the-us/.

6.   "World Energy Investment 2017 : Key Findings". 2019. *IEA.org*. Accessed January 17 2019.
     https://www.iea.org/publications/wei2017/.

7.   "New Tech Could Transform The $2 Trillion Auto Industry". 2019. *PRNewswire.Com*.
     Accessed January 17 2019. https://www.prnewswire.com/news-releases/new-tech-could-
     transform-the-2-trillion-auto-industry-673561583.html.

8.   McCarthy, Nial. "Renewable Energy Employment: How China And The U.S. Measure Up
     [Infographic]". 2017. *Forbes.com*. Accessed January 17 2019. https://www.forbes.com/sites/
     niallmccarthy/2017/06/23/renewable-energy-employment-how-china-and-the-u-s-mea-
     sure-up-infographic/#23157f5b2679.

CHAPTER 2: A GLOBAL SHIFT

1.   McGrath, Matt. "US And China To Sign Climate Treaty". 2016. *BBC
     News*. Accessed January 17 2019. https://www.bbc.com/news/
     science-environment-35935756?ocid=global_bbccom_email_31032016_top+news+stories.

2.   Figueres, Christiana. 2019. "The Inside Story Of The Paris Climate Agree-
     ment". *TED.com*. Accessed January 17 2019. https://www.ted.com/talks/
     christiana_figueres_the_inside_story_of_the_paris_climate_agreement?language=en.

3.   Stern, Nicolas. *Government of the United Kingdom*. Accessed January 17 2019. http://mudan-
     casclimaticas.cptec.inpe.br/~rmclima/pdfs/destaques/sternreview_report_complete.pdf.

4.   Gillis, Justin, and Nadja Popovich. 2017. "The U.S. Is The Biggest Carbon Polluter In His-
     tory. It Just Walked Away From The Paris Climate Deal.". *Nytimes.com*. Accessed January
     17 2019. https://www.nytimes.com/interactive/2017/06/01/climate/us-biggest-carbon-pol-
     luter-in-history-will-it-walk-away-from-the-paris-climate-deal.html.

5.   Angres, Leigh, and Jorge Salazar. 2018. "The Federal Budget in 2017". *CBO.gov*. Accessed
     January 17 2019. https://www.cbo.gov/system/files?file=115th-congress-2017-2018/graph-
     ic/53624-fy17federalbudget.pdf.

6.   Leahy, Stephen. "Without The Ozone Treaty You'd Get Sunburned In 5 Minutes".
     2017. *News.Nationalgeographic.Com*. Accessed January 17 2019. https://news.nationalgeo-
     graphic.com/2017/09/montreal-protocol-ozone-treaty-30-climate-change-hcfs-hfcs/.

7.   "Ozone Layer On Track To Recovery: Success Story Should Encour-
     age Action On Climate". 2014. *UN Environment*. Accessed January 17
     2019. https://www.unenvironment.org/news-and-stories/press-release/
     ozone-layer-track-recovery-success-story-should-encourage-action.

8. Cama, Timothy. "Tillerson: 'My View Didn't Change' On Paris Climate Agreement". 2017. *The Hill.* Accessed January 17 2019. https://thehill.com/policy/energy-environment/337578-tillerson-my-view-didnt-change-on-paris-climate-agreement.

9. "Statement By President Trump On The Paris Climate Accord | The White House". 2017. *The White House.* Accessed January 17 2019. https://www.whitehouse.gov/briefings-statements/statement-president-trump-paris-climate-accord/.

10. Abrams, Abigail. "Pittsburgh Mayor Bill Peduto Hits Back at President Trump: 'We Will Follow the Guidelines of the Paris Agreement'". 2019. *Time.* Accessed January 17 2019. http://time.com/4802340/paris-agreement-pittsburgh-mayor-bill-peduto-donald-trump/.

11. "Paris Climate Agreement – Climate Mayors". 2018. *ClimateMayors.org.* Accessed January 17 2019. http://climatemayors.org/actions/paris-climate-agreement/.

12. Barrón-López, Laura. "Republicans Who Support Combating Climate Change Urge Trump To Stay In Paris Deal". 2017. *Huffpost UK.* Accessed January 17 2019. https://www.huffingtonpost.com/entry/republicans-climate-change_us_592f1825e4b09ec37c314856.

13. "EU-CHINA LEADERS' STATEMENT ON CLIMATE CHANGE AND CLEAN ENERGY". 2018. *Ec.Europa.eu.* Accessed January 17 2019. https://ec.europa.eu/clima/sites/clima/files/news/20180713_statement_en.pdf.

14. Huang, Echo, and Tripti Lahiri. "Xi Jinping To China: "Any Harm We Inflict On Nature Will Eventually Return To Haunt Us"". 2017. *Quartz.* Accessed January 17 2019. https://qz.com/1105119/watch-what-xi-jinpings-19th-chinese-communist-party-congress-work-report-said-on-climate-change/.

15. "Baseline And Doubling Plans – Mission Innovation". 2019. *Mission-Innovation.Net.* Accessed January 17 2019. http://mission-innovation.net/our-work/baseline-and-doubling-plans/.

16. "Strategies, Progress, Plans, and Funding Information Submitted by Mission Innovation Members." 2019. *Mission-Innovation.net.* Accessed January 17 2019. http://mission-innovation.net/wp-content/uploads/2016/06/MI-Country-Plans-and-Priorities.pdf.

17. "Breakthrough Energy - Investing In A Carbonless Future". 2019. *Breakthrough Energy.* Accessed January 17 2019. http://www.b-t.energy/.

18. Korosec, Kirsten. "John Doerr On Why He Joined Bill Gates' Billion Dollar Energy Fund". 2019. *Fortune.* Accessed January 17 2019. http://fortune.com/2016/12/21/john-doerr-on-why-he-joined-bill-gates-billion-dollar-energy-fund/.

19. Alvarado, Laura. "Costa Rica Has Run Almost Entirely On Clean Energy For The Past Four Years - Costa Rica Star News". 2018. *Costa Rica Star News.* Accessed January 17 2019. https://news.co.cr/costa-rica-has-run-almost-entirely-on-clean-energy-for-the-past-four-years/74423/.

20. Irfan, Umair. "Costa Rica Has An Ambitious New Climate Policy — But No, It'S Not Banning Fossil Fuels". 2018. *Vox.* Accessed January 17 2019. https://www.vox.com/energy-and-environment/2018/7/17/17568190/costa-rica-renewable-energy-fossil-fuels-transportation.

21. Roberts, David. "UK Emissions Are Falling Fast. Now The Country Might Try For Zero". 2018. *Vox.* Accessed January 17 2019. https://www.vox.com/energy-and-environment/2018/4/18/17185496/uk-climate-change-g7-coal-emissions.

22. "UK Energy in Brief 2017". 2017. *UK's Department for Business, Energy, & Industrial Strategy.* Accessed January 17 2019. https://assets.publishing.service.gov.uk/government/uploads/system/uploads/attachment_data/file/631146/UK_Energy_in_Brief_2017.pdf.

23. Rathi, Akshat. "A Carbon Tax Killed Coal In The UK. Natural Gas Is Next.". 2018. *Quartz.* Accessed January 17 2019. https://qz.com/1192753/a-carbon-tax-killed-coal-in-the-uk-natural-gas-is-next/.

24. "France - Energy System Overview". 2019. *IEA.org.* Accessed January 17 2019. https://www.iea.org/media/countries/France.pdf.

25. "Nuclear Power In France | French Nuclear Energy - World Nuclear Association". 2019. *World-Nuclear.Org.* Accessed January 17 2019. http://www.world-nuclear.org/information-library/country-profiles/countries-a-f/france.aspx.

26. Gustin, Georgina. "U.S. Power Plant Emissions Fall To Near 1990 Levels". 2017. *Insideclimate News.* Accessed January 17 2019. https://insideclimatenews.org/news/14062017/us-power-plant-co2-carbon-emissions-fall-1990-ceres.

27. "Apple Now Globally Powered By 100 Percent Renewable Energy". 2019. *Apple.* Accessed January 17 2019. https://www.apple.com/newsroom/2018/04/apple-now-globally-powered-by-100-percent-renewable-energy/.

28. "Apple Launches New Clean Energy Fund In China". 2019. *Apple.* Accessed January 17 2019. https://www.apple.com/newsroom/2018/07/apple-launches-new-clean-energy-fund-in-china/.

29. Pyper, Julia. "Google Officially Hits Its 100% Renewable Energy Target". 2019. *Greentechmedia.* Accessed January 17 2019. https://www.greentechmedia.com/articles/read/google-officially-hits-100-renewable-energy-target#gs.2Q3Baq4N.

30. Beer, Jeff. "Budweiser's New Symbol Stands For Every Beer Made With 100% Renewable Energy". 2018. *Fast Company.* Accessed January 17 2019. https://www.fastcompany.com/40519988/budweisers-new-symbol-stands-for-every-beer-made-with-100-renewable-energy.

31. "Companies - RE100". 2019. *There100.org.* Accessed January 17 2019. http://there100.org/companies.

32. DiChristopher, Tom. 2018. "Electric Vehicles Will Grow From 3 Million To 125 Million By 2030, International Energy Agency Forecasts". *CNBC.* Accessed January 17 2019. https://www.cnbc.com/2018/05/30/electric-vehicles-will-grow-from-3-million-to-125-million-by-2030-iea.html.

33. Chrisafis, Angelique, and Adam Vaughan. 2017. "France To Ban Sales Of Petrol And Diesel Cars By 2040". *The Guardian.* Accessed January 17 2019. https://www.theguardian.com/business/2017/jul/06/france-ban-petrol-diesel-cars-2040-emmanuel-macron-volvo.

34. Asthana, Anushka, and Matthew Taylor. 2017. "Britain To Ban Sale Of All Diesel And Petrol Cars And Vans From 2040". *The Guardian.* Accessed January 17 2019. https://www.theguardian.com/politics/2017/jul/25/britain-to-ban-sale-of-all-diesel-and-petrol-cars-and-vans-from-2040.

35. Knudsen, Camilla, and Alister Doyle. "Norway Powers Ahead (Electrically): Over Half New Car Sales Now Electric or Hybrid". 2019. *Reuters.* Accessed January 17 2019. https://www.reuters.com/article/us-environment-norway-autos/norway-powers-ahead-over-half-new-car-sales-now-electric-or-hybrid-idUSKBN1ES0WC.

36. Jolly, David. "Norway Is A Model For Encouraging Electric Car Sales". 2019. *NYTimes. Com*. Accessed January 17 2019. https://www.nytimes.com/2015/10/17/business/international/norway-is-global-model-for-encouraging-sales-of-electric-cars.html.

37. "Facts At A Glance". 2019. *Metro.Net*. Accessed January 17 2019. https://www.metro.net/news/facts-glance/.

38. Wei, Katherine. "When It Comes To Electric Buses, China Is Killing It". 2018. *Sierra Club*. Accessed January 17 2019. https://www.sierraclub.org/sierra/when-it-comes-electric-buses-china-killing-it.

39. Ren, Daniel. "China's Technology Hub Has An All-Electric Bus Fleet, Funded By The State". 2018. *South China Morning Post*. Accessed January 17 2019. https://www.scmp.com/business/china-business/article/2169709/shenzhens-all-electric-bus-fleet-worlds-first-comes-massive.

40. Marshall, Aarian. 2017. "Volvo's Electric Car Plan Isn't As Bold Or Crazy As It Seems". *WIRED*. Accessed January 17 2019. https://www.wired.com/story/volvos-electric-car-plan/.

41. Mitchell, Russ. 2017. "BMW Plans 25 All-Electric And Hybrid Vehicles By 2025; Jaguar Shows Off Electric E-Type". *Latimes.Com*. Accessed January 17 2019. https://www.latimes.com/business/autos/la-fi-hy-bmw-jaguar-ev-20170907-story.html.

42. "GM's Path To An All-Electric, Zero Emissions Future". 2018. *GM.Com*. Accessed January 17 2019. https://media.gm.com/media/us/en/gm/home.detail.html/content/Pages/news/us/en/2018/mar/0307-barra-speech.html.

43. Hawkins, Andrew. "Uber Will Start Paying Some Drivers To Switch To Electric Cars". 2018. *The Verge*. Accessed January 17 2019. https://www.theverge.com/2018/6/19/17480044/uber-electric-vehicle-ev-driver-cash-incentive.

44. Matousek, Mark. "Tesla Has A New Customer For Its Electric Semi — Here Are All The Companies That Have Ordered The Big Rig". 2018. *Business Insider*. Accessed January 17 2019. https://www.businessinsider.com/companies-that-ordered-tesla-semi-2017-12.

45. Lambert, Fred. 2018. "Tesla Semi Receives Order Of 30 More Electric Trucks From Walmart". *Electrek*. Accessed January 17 2019. https://electrek.co/2018/09/06/tesla-semi-new-order-electric-truck-walmart/.

CHAPTER 3: CHINA'S GLOBAL AMBITIONS

1. "Innovation In China: George Yip & Bruce Mckern". 2016. *Yale School Of Management*. Accessed January 17 2019. https://som.yale.edu/faculty-research/our-centers-initiatives/center-customer-insights/events/event/2016/04/innovation-china-george-yip-bruce-mckern.

2. "'Airpocalypse' Over? Beijing Breathes Easier As Clean Air Drive Pays Off". 2018. *South China Morning Post*. Accessed January 17 2019. https://www.scmp.com/news/china/policies-politics/article/2160444/beijings-clean-air-drive-paying-swift-recovery.

3. Day, Esha. "Here's How Many People Die Each Day In China Because Of Its Filthy Air". 2015. *VICE News*. Accessed January 17 2019. https://news.vice.com/en_us/article/j5987p/heres-how-many-people-die-each-day-in-china-because-of-its-filthy-air.

4. Wong, Edward. "China Blocks Web Access To 'Under The Dome' Documentary On Pollution". 2015. *Nytimes.Com*. Accessed January 17 2019. https://www.nytimes.com/2015/03/07/world/asia/china-blocks-web-access-to-documentary-on-nations-air-pollution.html.

5. "Technical note on estimates of infrastructure investment needs". 2017. *OECD.org*. Accessed January 17 2019. https://www.oecd.org/env/cc/g20-climate/Technical-note-estimates-of-infrastructure-investment-needs.pdf.

6. Allison, Graham. 2017. "What Xi Jinping Wants". *The Atlantic*. Accessed January 17 2019. https://www.theatlantic.com/international/archive/2017/05/what-china-wants/528561/.

7. Laskai, Lorand. "Why Does Everyone Hate Made In China 2025?". 2019. *Council On Foreign Relations*. Accessed January 17 2019. https://www.cfr.org/blog/why-does-everyone-hate-made-china-2025.

8. Kennedy, Scott. "Made In China 2025". 2015. *Csis.Org*. Accessed January 17 2019. https://www.csis.org/analysis/made-china-2025.

9. "Escaping the Middle Income Trap". 2013. *Global Economic Symposium*. Accessed January 17 2019. https://www.global-economic-symposium.org/knowledgebase/escaping-the-middle-income-trap.

10. Martina, Yao, and Chen. "Exclusive: Facing U.S. Blowback, Beijing Softens 'Made In China' Message". 2019. *U.S.*. Accessed January 17 2019. https://www.reuters.com/article/us-usa-trade-china-madeinchina2025-exclu/exclusive-facing-u-s-blowback-beijing-softens-made-in-china-2025-message-idUSKBN1JL12U.

11. "Trump Says Would Intervene In Arrest Of Chinese Executive". 2018. *Reuters*. Accessed January 17 2019. https://www.reuters.com/article/us-usa-trump/trump-says-would-intervene-in-arrest-of-chinese-executive-idUSKBN1OB01P.

12. Masters, Jonathan, and James McBride. "Foreign Investment And U.S. National Security". 2018. *Council On Foreign Relations*. Accessed January 17 2019. https://www.cfr.org/backgrounder/foreign-investment-and-us-national-security.

13. McBride, James. "Is 'Made In China 2025' A Threat To Global Trade?". 2018. *Council On Foreign Relations*. Accessed January 17 2019. https://www.cfr.org/backgrounder/made-china-2025-threat-global-trade.

14. "China's Bountiful Gift to Volkswagen?". 2018. *Bloomberg.com*. Accessed January 17 2019. https://www.bloomberg.com/opinion/articles/2018-04-17/china-s-bounty-is-lovely-for-tesla-less-so-for-volkswagen.

15. "What Is China's Belt And Road Initiative?". 2017. *The Economist*. Accessed January 17 2019. https://www.economist.com/the-economist-explains/2017/05/14/what-is-chinas-belt-and-road-initiative.

16. "Belt And Road Initiative". 2018. *World Bank*. Accessed January 18 2019. https://www.worldbank.org/en/topic/regional-integration/brief/belt-and-road-initiative.

17. Abi-Habib, Maria. "How China Got Sri Lanka To Cough Up A Port". 2018. *NYTimes.com*. Accessed January 18 2019. https://www.nytimes.com/2018/06/25/world/asia/china-sri-lanka-port.html.

18. Heide, Hoppe, Scheuer, and Stratmann. 2018. "EU Ambassadors Band Together Against Silk Road". *Handelsblatt.Com*. Accessed January 18 2019. https://www.handelsblatt.com/today/politics/china-first-eu-ambassadors-band-together-against-silk-road/23581860.html?ticket=ST-757583-6sH67uIKANSvjnsxzJ92-ap5.

19. "Highlights of Proposals for China's 13ᵗʰ Five Year Plan". 2015. *Xinhua*. Accessed January 18 2019. http://www.xinhuanet.com//english/photo/2015-11/04/c_134783513.htm.

20. "China Regulates Environmental Audits". 2017. *Xinhuanet.com*. Accessed January 18 2019. http://www.xinhuanet.com/english/2017-11/28/c_136785927.htm.

21. "China Focus: Environmental Audits To Decide Official Promotions". 2017. *Xinhuanet.Com*. Accessed January 19 2019. http://www.xinhuanet.com/english/2017-07/06/c_136422947.htm.

22. Rajeev, Puja. "How China became a global leader in green finance". 2018. *Eco-Business*. Accessed January 18 2019. https://www.eco-business.com/news/how-china-became-a-global-leader-in-green-finance/

23. Cao, Cong. "China's 15-year science and technology plan". 2006. *University of Oregon*. Accessed January 18 2019. https://china-us.uoregon.edu/pdf/final%20print%20version.pdf.

24. "Research And Development Expenditure (% Of GDP) | Data". 2019. *Data.WorldBank.Org*. Accessed January 18 2019. https://data.worldbank.org/indicator/GB.XPD.RSDV.GD.ZS?end=2015&locations=CN-US&start=1996&view=chart.

25. "New Renewable Energy Investments Made By Top 10 Countries ". 2018. *Atlas*. Accessed January 18 2019. https://www.theatlas.com/charts/ry7bvDusz.

CHAPTER 4: CHINA'S DISRUPTION IN CLEAN ENERGY

1.   Cheng, Evelyn. 2018. "Tesla's China Factory Is Set To Begin Production Late Next Year, Shanghai Government Says". *CNBC*. Accessed January 18 2019. https://www.cnbc.com/2018/12/06/teslas-china-factory-set-to-begin-production-late-next-year.html.

2.   Wieczner, Jen. "GM's Mary Barra Makes a U-Turn on China". 2017. *Fortune*. Accessed January 18 2019. http://fortune.com/2017/10/10/gm-electric-cars-china/.

3.   Roberts, David. "Scientists Assessed The Options For Growing Nuclear Power. They Are Grim.". 2018. *Vox*. Accessed January 18 2019. https://www.vox.com/energy-and-environment/2018/7/11/17555644/nuclear-power-energy-climate-decarbonization-renewables.

4.   England, Rachel. "China Bumps Up Renewable Energy Target To Reduce Reliance On Coal". 2018. *Engadget*. Accessed January 18 2019. https://www.engadget.com/2018/09/26/china-raises-renewable-energy-target-to-reduce-coal/.

5.   State Grid Corporation of China. 2016. "Global Energy Interconnection: Vision Of A World Power Grid". *PRNewswire.com*. Accessed January 18 2019. https://www.prnewswire.com/news-releases/global-energy-interconnection-vision-of-a-world-power-grid-300238674.html.

6.   Patel, Sonal. "China Sets A New Renewable Portfolio Standard". 2018. *POWER Magazine*. Accessed January 18 2019. https://www.powermag.com/china-sets-a-new-renewable-portfolio-standard/.

7.   Chung, Horowitz, and Kurup. "Emerging Opportunities and Challenges in U.S. Solar Manufacturing" 2016. *NREL.gov*. Accessed January 18 2019. https://www.nrel.gov/docs/fy16osti/65788.pdf.

8.   "2018 Top 10 Solar Panel Manufacturers & Companies In China". 2019. *Tunto Green Power*. Accessed January 18 2019. https://www.tuntopower.com/solar-panel-manufacturers-companies/.

9.   "10 Top Solar Panel Companies & Manufacturers For 2019 | EnergySage". 2019. *Solar News*. Accessed January 18 2019. https://news.energysage.com/best-solar-panel-manufacturers-usa/.

10.   Mathis, Karen. 2018. "JinkoSolar Launches Pilot Production At Jacksonville Plant". *WJCT.org*. Accessed January 18 2019. http://news.wjct.org/post/jinkosolar-launches-pilot-production-jacksonville-plant.

11.   Aleem, Zeeshan. "Donald Trump Has Finally Dealt His First Blow To China's Economy". 2018. *Vox*. Accessed January 18 2019. https://www.vox.com/world/2018/1/23/16920984/solar-panel-china-trump-tariff-washers-south-korea.

12.   Sandalow, David. "Guide To China Policy 2018". 2018. *Columbia*. Accessed January 18 2019. https://energypolicy.columbia.edu/sites/default/files/pictures/Guide%20to%20Chinese%20Climate%20Policy%207-27-18.pdf.

13.   "30 Years of Policies for Wind Energy". 2019. *IRENA*. Accessed January 18 2019. https://www.irena.org/documentdownloads/publications/gwec_china.pdf.

14.   "Top Ten Turbine Makers Of 2017". 2017. *WindPowerMonthly.com*. Accessed January 18 2019. https://www.windpowermonthly.com/article/1445638/top-ten-turbine-makers-2017.

15.   "Goldwind Americas Signs 60MW Wind Turbine Supply Orders With One Energy". 2017. *Prnewswire.Com*. Accessed January 18 2019. https://www.prnewswire.com/news-releases/goldwind-americas-signs-60mw-wind-turbine-supply-orders-with-one-energy-300500369.html.

16.   Efstathiou, Jim. "Trump's Import Tariffs Will Make U.S. Wind Power More Expensive". 2018. *Bloomberg.com*. Accessed January 18 2019. https://www.bloomberg.com/news/articles/2018-10-02/trump-s-import-tariffs-will-make-u-s-wind-power-more-expensive.

17.   "Hydropower | Guide To Chinese Climate Policy". 2019. *Columbia*. Accessed January 18 2019. https://chineseclimatepolicy.energypolicy.columbia.edu/en/hydropower.

18.   Jensen-Cormier, Stephanie. "Reflections On Chinese Companies' Global Investments In The Hydropower Sector Between 2006-2017". 2017. *International Rivers*. Accessed January 18 2019. https://www.internationalrivers.org/blogs/435/reflections-on-chinese-companies%E2%80%99-global-investments-in-the-hydropower-sector-between-2006.

19.   Nathanson, Max. 2018. "How To Respond To Chinese Investment In Latin America". *Foreign Policy*. Accessed January 18 2019. https://foreignpolicy.com/2018/11/28/how-to-respond-to-chinese-investment-in-latin-america/.

20. "China Nuclear Power | Chinese Nuclear Energy - World Nuclear Association". 2019. *World-Nuclear.org*. Accessed January 18 2019. http://www.world-nuclear.org/information-library/country-profiles/countries-a-f/china-nuclear-power.aspx.

21. Evans, Scarlett. 2018. "Is China Powering The Future Of Nuclear?". *Power Technology*. Accessed January 18 2019. https://www.power-technology.com/features/future-of-nuclear-china/.

22. "The ETI Nuclear Cost Drivers Project: Summary Report | The ETI". 2019. *The ETI*. Accessed January 18 2019. https://www.eti.co.uk/library/the-eti-nuclear-cost-drivers-project-summary-report.

23. Wood, Zoe. 2018. "China Looking To Buy Stake In UK Nuclear Plants, Say Reports". *The Guardian*. Accessed January 18 2019. https://www.theguardian.com/environment/2018/jul/08/china-interested-majority-stake-uk-nuclear-power-stations-reports.

24. Davies, Rob. 2016. "China-UK Investment: Key Questions Following Hinkley Point C Delay". *The Guardian*. Accessed January 18 2019. https://www.theguardian.com/business/2016/aug/09/china-uk-investment-key-questions-following-hinkley-point-c-delay.

25. Ichord, Robert. "US Nuclear-Power Leadership and the Chinese and Russian Challenge". 2018. *AtlanticCouncil.org*. Accessed January 18 2019. https://www.atlanticcouncil.org/images/publications/US_Nuclear-Power_Leadership_web.pdf.

26. Zinan, Cao. "Why China's 'Artificial Sun' Bodes Well For Energy Of The Future". 2018. *The Telegraph*. Accessed January 18 2019. https://www.telegraph.co.uk/news/world/china-watch/technology/nuclear-fusion-reactor/.

27. Kaku, Michio. "Fusion Really Is 20 Years Away". 2019. *Big Think*. Accessed January 18 2019. https://bigthink.com/surprising-science/china-nuclear-fusion-reactor-100-million-degrees?rebelltitem=3#rebelltitem3.

28. Reilly, Michael. "A Thorium-Salt Reactor Has Fired Up For The First Time In Four Decades". 2017. *MIT Technology Review*. Accessed January 18 2019. https://www.technologyreview.com/the-download/608712/a-thorium-salt-reactor-has-fired-up-for-the-first-time-in-four-decades/.

29. Hanley, Steve. 2018. "China Making Big Battery Storage Push In 2019 | Cleantechnica". *Cleantechnica*. Accessed January 18 2019. https://cleantechnica.com/2018/12/27/china-making-big-battery-storage-push-in-2019/.

30. Colthrope, Andy. "China's Biggest Flow Battery Project So Far Is Underway With Hundreds More Megawatts To Come". 2018. *Energy Storage News*. Accessed January 18 2019. https://www.energy-storage.news/news/chinas-biggest-flow-battery-project-so-far-is-underway-with-hundreds-more-m.

31. "Bloomberg NEF | About Us". 2019. *Bloomberg NEF*. Accessed January 18 2019. https://about.bnef.com/about/.

32. "New Energy Outlook 2018". 2019. *Turtl.Co*. Accessed January 18 2019. https://bnef.turtl.co/story/neo2018?teaser=true.

CHAPTER 5: CHINA'S DISRUPTION IN CLEAN MOBILITY

1. Wieczner, Jen. "GM's Mary Barra Makes a U-Turn on China". 2017. *Fortune*. Accessed January 18 2019. http://fortune.com/2017/10/10/gm-electric-cars-china/.

2. Coren, Michael. "For The First Time, A Chinese Car Is Coming To The US—And It's Electric". 2018. *Quartz*. Accessed January 18 2019. https://qz.com/1500303/chinas-qiantu-will-be-first-chinese-electric-carmaker-to-challenge-tesla-in-the-us/.

3. Coren, Michael. "Nine Countries Say They'll Ban Internal Combustion Engines. So Far, It's Just Words.". 2018. *Quartz*. Accessed January 18 2019. https://qz.com/1341155/nine-countries-say-they-will-ban-internal-combustion-engines-none-have-a-law-to-do-so/.

4. Perkowski, Jack. "What's In Store For China's Auto Industry This Year? 2017 Provided Some Clues". 2018. *Forbes.com*. Accessed January 18 2019. https://www.forbes.com/sites/jackperkowski/2018/02/07/china-autos-a-2017-wrap-up-and-2018-preview/#4a1cb0ab3bce.

5. Ren, Daniel. "China's Technology Hub Has An All-Electric Bus Fleet, Funded By The State". 2018. *South China Morning Post*. Accessed January 18 2019. https://www.scmp.com/business/china-business/article/2169709/shenzhens-all-electric-bus-fleet-worlds-first-comes-massive.

6. "Electric Vehicles". 2019. *Bloomberg New Energy Finance*. Accessed January 18 2019. https://bnef.turtl.co/story/evo2018?teaser=true.

7. "Future of the vehicle". 2017. *BlackRock.com*. Accessed January 18 2019. https://www.blackrock.com/investing/literature/whitepaper/bii-future-of-vehicle-2017-us.pdf.

CHAPTER 6: AMERICA'S ECOSHOT

1. Lafleur, Claude. "The Space Review: Costs Of US Piloted Programs". 2019. *TheSpaceReview.com*. Accessed January 18 2019. http://www.thespacereview.com/article/1579/1.

2. "Impact Of The Semiconductor Industry". 2019. *Semiconductor Industry Association*. Accessed January 18 2019. https://www.semiconductors.org/semiconductors-101/industry-impact/.

3. "About The Human Genome Project". 2019. *ORNL.gov*. Accessed January 18 2019. https://web.ornl.gov/sci/techresources/Human_Genome/project/index.shtml.

4. "Human Genome Project Completion: Frequently Asked Questions". 2019. *National Human Genome Research Institute*. Accessed January 18 2019. https://www.genome.gov/11006943/human-genome-project-completion-frequently-asked-questions/.

5. "Economic Impact of the Human Genome Project". 2011. *Battelle.org*. Accessed January 18 2019. https://www.battelle.org/docs/default-source/misc/battelle-2011-misc-economic-impact-human-genome-project.pdf?sfvrsn=6.

6. "Summary For Policymakers — Global Warming Of 1.5 ºC". 2019. *IPCC.ch*. Accessed January 18 2019. https://www.ipcc.ch/sr15/chapter/summary-for-policy-makers/.

CHAPTER 7: AMERICAN SCIENTISTS

1. Trembath, Jenkins, Nordhaus, and Shellenberger. "Where the Shale Revolution Came From". 2012. *The Breakthrough Institute*. Accessed January 18 2019. https://s3.us-east-2. amazonaws.com/uploads.thebreakthrough.org/legacy/blog/Where_the_Shale_Gas_Revolution_Came_From.pdf.

2. "EERE Success Story—Battery Cathode Developed By Argonne Powers Plug-In Electric Vehicles". 2019. *Energy.Gov*. Accessed January 18 2019. https://www.energy.gov/eere/success-stories/articles/ eere-success-story-battery-cathode-developed-argonne-powers-plug.

3. "10 Amazing DARPA Inventions". 2019. *Alphr*. Accessed January 18 2019. https://www. alphr.com/features/373546/10-brilliant-darpa-inventions.

4. "Mission". *DARPA.mil*. Accessed January 18 2019. https://www.darpa.mil/about-us/mission.

5. "Rising Above the Gathering Storm: Energizing and Employing America for a Brighter Economic Future". 2007. *WSU.edu*. Accessed January 18 2019. https://s3.wp.wsu.edu/ uploads/sites/618/2015/11/Rising-Above-the-Gathering-Storm.pdf.

6. Irfan, Umair. "Trump Wanted To Slash Funding For Clean Energy. Congress Ignored Him.". 2018. *Vox*. Accessed January 18 2019. https://www.vox.com/ energy-and-environment/2018/3/22/17151352/omnibus-energy-environment-trump.

7. "Congressional Comment From U.S. Senator Lamar Alexander". 2019. *ARPA-E*. Accessed January 18 2019. https://www.youtube.com/watch?v=d1LfDruMZxY.

8. "The Sunshot Initiative". 2019. *Energy.gov*. Accessed January 18 2019. https://www.energy. gov/eere/solar/sunshot-initiative.

9. "Experience Curve". *Policonomics.com*. Accessed January 18 2019. https://policonomics. com/experience-curve/.

10. "Learning & Experience Curves In Manufacturing". 2019. *Strategosinc.Com*. Accessed January 18 2019. http://www.strategosinc.com/articles/strategy/learning_curves.htm.

11. "Budget". 2014. *National Institutes Of Health*. Accessed January 18 2019. https://www.nih. gov/about-nih/what-we-do/budget.

12. "From Lab Bench To Bedside: A Backgrounder On Drug Development". 2014. *Pewtrusts. Org*. Accessed January 18 2019. https://www.pewtrusts.org/en/research-and-analysis/ articles/2014/03/12/from-lab-bench-to-bedside-a-backgrounder-on-drug-development.

13. "Loan Guarantee Program". 2019. *SEIA*. Accessed January 18 2019. https://www.seia.org/ initiatives/loan-guarantee-program.

14. Wesoff, Eric. "Are DOE Loan Guarantees An Energy Policy Mistake?". 2011. *Greentechmedia.Com*. Accessed January 18 2019. https://www.greentechmedia.com/articles/read/ are-doe-loan-guarantees-an-energy-policy-mistake#gs.U3STY5MJ.

15. "Tesla Gets Loan Approval From US Department Of Energy". 2010. *Tesla*. Accessed January 18 2019. https://www.tesla.com/blog/tesla-gets-loan-approval-us-department-energy.

16. "Tesla Repays Department Of Energy Loan Nine Years Early". 2013. *Tesla*. Accessed January 18 2019. https://www.tesla.com/blog/tesla-repays-department-energy-loan-nine-years-early.

17. Baker, David. 2018. "Tesla To Cut 9 Percent Of Workforce But Will Spare Factory". *SFchronicle.Com*. Accessed January 18 2019. https://www.sfchronicle.com/business/article/Tesla-to-cut-9-percent-of-workforce-but-spares-12988106.php.

18. "Alamosa". 2019. *Energy.gov*. Accessed January 18 2019. https://www.energy.gov/lpo/alamosa.

CHAPTER 8: AMERICAN INVESTORS

1.   "About Us". 2018. *Clean Tax Cuts*. Accessed January 18 2019. https://cleantaxcuts.org/about/.

2.   Johnson, Lacey. "Should We Just Get Rid Of Auto Efficiency Regulations Altogether?". 2018. *Greentechmedia.Com*. Accessed January 18 2019. https://www.greentechmedia.com/articles/read/a-new-free-market-policy-for-auto-fuel-efficiency.

3.   Volcovici, Valerie. "Apple Issues $1.5 Billion In Green Bonds In First Sale". 2019. *Reuters*. Accessed January 18 2019. https://www.reuters.com/article/us-apple-greenbonds/apple-issues-1-5-billion-in-green-bonds-in-first-sale-idUSKCN0VQ2K2.

4.   "Apple Inc. Green Bond". 2017. *Sustainalytics.com*. Accessed January 18 2019. http://www.sustainalytics.com/wp-content/uploads/2017/06/Green-Bond-Framework-and-Second-Opinion-Apple2017-final.pdf.

5.   "Clean Tax Cuts for Green Bonds – Charrette Summary". *Cleantaxcuts.Org*. Accessed January 18 2019. https://cleantaxcuts.org/wp-content/uploads/char-sum-greenbonds-bradford-170306.pdf.

6.   "The Mechanics Of Rate Of Return Regulation". *PSU.edu*. Accessed January 18 2019. https://www.e-education.psu.edu/eme801/node/531.

7.   Walker, Paul. "Zero Regrets Energy & Tax Policy". *ConservAmerica*. Accessed January 18 2019. http://conservamerica.org/wp-content/uploads/2017/01/Zero-Regrets-Energy-Policy-v2.pdf.

8.   "Clean Tax Cuts for Commercial Real Estate". 2017. *CleanTaxCuts.org*. Accessed January 18 2019. https://cleantaxcuts.org/wp-content/uploads/char-sum-realestate-170610-170323.pdf.

9.   "Clean Tax Cuts For The Automotive Industry". *CleanTaxCuts.org*. Accessed January 18 2019. https://cleantaxcuts.org/wp-content/uploads/char-sum-transp-ct-c4auto-170610-170414.pdf.

10. "The Emerging Energy Technology Credit". *CleanCapitalistCoalition.org*. Accessed January 18 2019. https://cleancapitalistcoalition.org/wp-content/uploads/2018/09/The-Emerging-Energy-Technology-Credit-Summary.pdf.

11. "Issue Brief: Master Limited Partnerships". *CRESforum.org*. Accessed January 18 2019. https://cresforum.org/wp-content/uploads/2018/11/CRES_Forum_Master_Limited_Partnerships_web.pdf.

12. "Federal Tax Credits For Electric And Plug-In Hybrid Cars". 2018. *FuelEconomy.gov*. Accessed January 18 2019. https://www.fueleconomy.gov/feg/taxevb.shtml.

13. Lambert, Fred. 2018. "New Bill To Remove Limit For $7.5K Electric Vehicle Federal Tax Credit Introduced As Tesla Hits Threshold". *Electrek*. Accessed January 18 2019. https://electrek.co/2018/07/02/new-bill-electric-car-federal-tax-credit-tesla-limit/.

14. "The Climate Solutions Caucus". 2018. *Citizens' Climate Lobby*. Accessed January 18 2019. https://citizensclimatelobby.org/climate-solutions-caucus/.

15. Luper, Katie. 2018. "PFD For 2018 Is Set For $1,600". *Webcenter11.Com*. Accessed January 18 2019. https://www.webcenter11.com/content/news/PFD-for-2018-is-set-for-1600-492458361.html.

16. "National Survey Results on the Baker-Shultz Carbon Dividends Plan – October 2018". 2018. *CLCouncil.Org*. Accessed January 18 2019. https://www.clcouncil.org/media/YaleG-MU-Poll-October-2018.pdf.

17. "National Survey Results on the Baker-Shultz Carbon Dividends Plan – Released in September 2018". 2018. *CLCouncil.org*. Accessed January 18 2019. https://www.clcouncil.org/media/Baker-Shultz-Carbon-Dividends-Plan-Survey-Results.pdf.

18. Mufson, Steven. "ExxonMobil gives $1 million to promote a carbon tax-and-dividend plan". 2018. *The Washington Post*. Accessed January 18 2019. https://www.washingtonpost.com/energy-environment/2018/10/09/exxonmobil-gives-million-promote-carbon-tax-and-dividend-plan/.

19. "Lobbying Spending Database Oil & Gas, 2018". *OpenSecrets.org*. Accessed January 18 2019. https://www.opensecrets.org/lobby/indusclient.php?id=E01.

CHAPTER 9: AMERICAN BUSINESSES

1. "47 CFR 1.4000 - Restrictions Impairing Reception Of Television Broadcast Signals, Direct Broadcast Satellite Services Or Multichannel Multipoint Distribution Services". *Cornell's Legal Information Institute*. Accessed January 18 2019. https://www.law.cornell.edu/cfr/text/47/

2. "Solar Automated Permit Processing". 2018. *TheSolarFoundation.org*. Accessed January 18 2019. http://www.thesolarfoundation.org/wp-content/uploads/2018/09/SolarAPP.pdf.

3. "4 Reasons Why Hydropower Is The Guardian Of The Grid". 2019. *Energy.gov*. Accessed January 18 2019. https://www.energy.gov/eere/articles/4-reasons-why-hydropower-guardian-grid.

4. "2017 Hydropower Market Report | Department Of Energy". 2018. *Energy.gov*. Accessed January 18 2019. https://www.energy.gov/eere/water/downloads/2017-hydropower-market-report.

5. Livingston, Randal. "Energy Supply Legislation". 2015. *Energy.Senate.Gov*. Accessed January 18 2019. https://www.energy.senate.gov/public/index.cfm/files/serve?File_id=cb6a58d3-df99-48af-beda-09ccfcdd7178.

6. Collins, John. "Discussion Drafts Addressing Hydropower Regulatory Modernization and FERC Process Coordination under the Natural Gas Act". 2019. *Hydro.Org*. Accessed January 18 2019. http://www.hydro.org/wp-content/uploads/2015/05/Cube-Hydro-Partners-EC-Hearing-Testimony.pdf.

7. "Hydropower". 2012. *ClearPath*. Accessed January 18 2019. https://clearpath.org/policy/hydropower/.

8. Conca, James. "Our Irrational Fear Of Radiation Is Costing Us -- And The Planet". 2016. *Forbes.Com*. Accessed January 18 2019. https://www.forbes.com/sites/jamesconca/2016/10/27/texting-while-driving-is-scary-radiation-should-not-be/#5aa1cbd83f83.

9. Glowatz, Elana. "Three Mile Island Accident Deaths, Location" 2018. *Newsweek*. Accessed January 18 2019. https://www.newsweek.com/three-mile-island-accident-deaths-location-facts-nuclear-meltdown-anniversary-864161.

10. Roberts, David. "Scientists Assessed The Options For Growing Nuclear Power. They Are Grim.". 2018. *Vox*. Accessed January 18 2019. https://www.vox.com/energy-and-environment/2018/7/11/17555644/nuclear-power-energy-climate-decarbonization-renewables.

11. "Bill Gates' Nuclear Venture Hits Snag Amid U.S. Restrictions On China Deals". 2019. *Reuters*. Accessed January 18 2019. https://www.reuters.com/article/us-terrapower-china/bill-gates-nuclear-venture-hits-snag-amid-u-s-restrictions-on-china-deals-wsj-idUSKCN1OV1S5.

12. "Nuclear". 2018. *ClearPath*. Accessed January 18 2019. https://clearpath.org/policy/nuclear/.

13. Egan, Matt. 2017. "Keystone XL Pipeline Would Create Jobs... 35 Permanent Ones". *CNNmoney*. Accessed January 18 2019. https://money.cnn.com/2017/03/24/investing/keystone-pipeline-jobs-trump/index.html.

14. "Derisking Decarbonization". 2017. *Stanford.edu*. Accessed January 18 2019. https://energy.stanford.edu/sites/default/files/stanfordcleanenergyfinanceframingdoc10-31_final.pdf.

CHAPTER 10: AMERICAN JOBS & COMMUNITIES

1. "Fastest Growing Occupations". 2019. *BLS.gov*. Accessed January 18 2019. https://www.bls.gov/emp/tables/fastest-growing-occupations.htm.

2. "Coal Data Browser". 2019. *EIA.gov*. Accessed January 18 2019. https://www.eia.gov/coal/data/browser/#/topic/33?agg=2,0,1&rank=g&geo=nvg1qag9vvlpnsoo&mntp=g&linechart=COAL.PRODUCTION.TOT-US-TOT.A&columnchart=COAL.PRODUCTION.TOT-US-TOT.A&map=COAL.PRODUCTION.TOT-US-TOT.A&freq=A&start=2015&end=2016&ctype=map%3Cype=pin&rtype=s&maptype=0&rse=0&pin=.

3. "Coalfield Development". 2018. *Coalfield Development*. Accessed January 18 2019. http://coalfield-development.org/.

4. "Huntington Herald-Dispatch: Rewire Appalachia To Train, Employ Displaced Coal Workers". 2016. *The WV Hub*. Accessed January 18 2019. http://wvhub.org/huntington-herald-dispatch-rewire-appalachia-to-train-employ-displaced-coal-workers/.

5. "The Partnerships For Opportunity And Workforce And Economic Revitalization (POWER) Initiative". 2015. *Whitehouse.Gov*. Accessed January 18 2019. https://obamawhitehouse.archives.gov/the-press-office/2015/03/27/fact-sheet-partnerships-opportunity-and-workforce-and-economic-revitaliz.

6. "Mid-Atlantic | GRID Alternatives". 2019. *GridAlternatives.org*. Accessed January 18 2019. https://gridalternatives.org/midatlantic.

7. "An Opportunity That Opens Promising Directions | GRID Alternatives News". 2018. *GridAlternatives.org*. Accessed January 18 2019. https://gridalternatives.org/regions/cv/news/opportunity-opens-promising-directions.

8. "GIA". 2019. *Design*. Accessed January 18 2019. https://www.greeniowaamericorps.org/.

9. "Weatherization Assistance Program". 2019. *Energy.Gov*. Accessed January 18 2019. https://www.energy.gov/eere/wipo/weatherization-assistance-program.

10. "Colorado Becomes First State To Install Solar As Part Of Weatherization Assistance Program ". 2016. *Energy.Gov*. Accessed January 18 2019. https://www.energy.gov/eere/articles/colorado-becomes-first-state-install-solar-part-weatherization-assistance-program.

11. "Low Income Community Energy Solutions | Department Of Energy". 2019. *Energy.gov*. Accessed January 18 2019. https://www.energy.gov/eere/slsc/low-income-community-energy-solutions.

12. "EERE Success Story—Part 2 – The Proof Is In The Savings". 2019. *Energy.gov*. Accessed January 18 2019. https://www.energy.gov/eere/success-stories/articles/eere-success-story-part-2-proof-savings.

13. "EERE Success Story—Part 2 – The Proof Is In The Savings". 2019. *Energy.Gov*. Accessed January 18 2019. https://www.energy.gov/eere/success-stories/articles/eere-success-story-part-2-proof-savings.

14. "Brighter Future: A Study On Solar In U.S. Schools". 2019. *SEIA*. Accessed January 18 2019. https://www.seia.org/research-resources/brighter-future-study-solar-us-schools-0.

15. Sylvia, Tim. 2018. "New York Announces Free Community Solar For 10,000 Low-Income Residents". *Pv Magazine USA*. Accessed January 18 2019. https://pv-magazine-usa.com/2018/12/06/new-york-announces-free-community-solar-for-10000-low-income-residents/.

16. "Fleet Electrification". *Seattle.gov*. Accessed January 18 2019. https://www.seattle.gov/Documents/Departments/FAS/FleetManagement/Fleet-Electrification.pdf.

17. "Paying For Electric Buses | U.S. PIRG". 2019. *Uspirg.org*. Accessed January 18 2019. https://uspirg.org/reports/usp/paying-electric-buses.

18. "Secretary Foxx And China'S Minister Of Transport Yang Chuangtang Kickoff The Race To Zero Emissions Challenge". 2016. *US Department Of Transportation*. Accessed January 18 2019. https://www.transportation.gov/briefing-room/secretary-foxx-and-chinas-minister-transport-yang-chuangtang-kickoff-race-zero.

19. "Page Not Found". *US Department Of Transportation*. Accessed January 18 2019. https://www.transportation.gov/R2ZE.

20. "Zero Emission Bus Overview". 2019. *Google Docs*. Accessed January 18 2019. https://drive.google.com/file/d/0B39YId14Zi1KcEZRboxjak5HR3A0MlVFUoFQMzVJcllRZTBJ/view.

21. "Low Or No Emission Vehicle Program - 5339(C)". 2019. *Federal Transit Administration*. Accessed January 18 2019. https://www.transit.dot.gov/funding/grants/lowno.

22. Schleifer, Theodore. «The Electric Bus Company Proterra Is Worth Up To $840 Million After Raising New Money». 2018. *Recode*. Accessed January 18 2019. https://www.recode.net/2018/5/24/17390640/proterra-electric-bus-fundraising-100-million.

23. Soule, Alexander. "Norwalk to pilot 'Uber for buses' concept". 2018. *Recode*. Accessed January 18 2019. https://www.thehour.com/business/article/Norwalk-to-pilot-Uber-for-buses-concept-12931813.php.

24. "Meet Olli · Local Motors". 2019. *Local Motors*. Accessed January 19 2019. https://localmotors.com/meet-olli/.

25. "Baidu Reaches New Milestone In Autonomous Driving With Volume Production Of China'S First Commercially Deployed Fully Autonomous Bus". 2018. *Globenewswire News Room*. Accessed January 19 2019. https://globenewswire.com/news-release/2018/07/04/1533216/0/en/Baidu-Reaches-New-Milestone-in-Autonomous-Driving-with-Volume-Production-of-China-s-First-Commercially-Deployed-Fully-Autonomous-Bus.html.

26. "How MPOs Use CMAQ Funding for Alterna9ve Fuel Vehicle and Infrastructure Projects". 2017. *Cleancities.Energy.Gov*. Accessed January 19 2019. https://cleancities.energy.gov/files/u/news_events/document/document_url/233/how-mpos-use-cmaq-funding-for-alternative-fuel-vehicle-and-infrastructure-projects.pdf.

27. "Governor Sandoval And NV Energy Announce The Nevada Electric Highway". 2019. *Energy.NV.gov*. Accessed January 19 2019. http://energy.nv.gov/Media/Press_Releases/2015/Governor_Sandoval_and_NV_Energy_Announce_the_Nevada_Electric_Highway/.

CHAPTER 11: POLICY LIST

1. "Dirty Energy Dominance: Dependent on Denail". 2017. *Oil Change International*. Accessed January 19 2019. http://priceofoil.org/content/uploads/2017/10/OCI_US-Fossil-Fuel-Subs-2015-16_Final_Oct2017.pdf.

2. Roberts, David. "Friendly Policies Keep US Oil And Coal Afloat Far More Than We Thought". 2017. *Vox*. Accessed January 19 2019. https://www.vox.com/energy-and-environment/2017/10/6/16428458/us-energy-coal-oil-subsidies.

3. "Fourth National Climate Assessment". 2018. *NCA2018.Globalchange.gov*. Accessed January 19 2019. https://nca2018.globalchange.gov/.

Made in the USA
Columbia, SC
22 May 2019